Visions of illness

An endography of real-time medical imaging

ISBN 978-90-5972-185-2

Uitgeverij Eburon
Postbus 2867
2601 CW Delft
tel.: 015-2131484 / fax: 015-2146888
info@eburon.nl / www.eburon.nl

Cover design: Studio Hermkens, Amsterdam

Visions of illness

An endography of real-time medical imaging

PROEFSCHRIFT

ter verkrijging van de graad van doctor aan de Universiteit Maastricht,
op gezag van de Rector Magnificus, Prof. mr. G.P.M.F. Mols
volgens het besluit van het College van Decanen,
in het openbaar te verdedigen
op donderdag 31 mei 2007 om 12:00 uur

door

Maud Radstake

geboren te Ede op 15 augustus 1973

Promotor:
        Prof. dr. J.F.T.M. van Dijck (Universiteit van Amsterdam)

Copromotor:
        Dr. B. Pasveer

Beoordelingscommissie:
        Prof. dr. ing. R. Zwijnenberg (voorzitter)
        Prof. dr. K. Horstman
        Prof. dr. A.M. Mol (Universiteit Twente)
        Dr. R. van de Vall
        Dr. ir. P.P.C.C. Verbeek (Universiteit Twente)

This research was supported by the Netherlands Organisation for Scientific Research (NWO).

The production of this book was supported by WTMC (The Netherlands Research School of Science, Technology and Modern Culture) and by the Faculty of Arts and Social Sciences of Maastricht University.

Acknowledgements

Five years of reading, thinking, discussing, watching and writing have resulted in this book. It also resulted in me being a doctor now. Writing the book was hard work; becoming a doctor has been great fun. There are many people to thank for their role in both creations.

The patients and professionals in the Departments of Radiology and Endoscopy where my fieldwork was situated, allowed me to be very close to their work and to their bodies. I thank them for their support and interest in my work.

José van Dijck and Bernike Pasveer, my supervisors, shaped my development as a researcher and made it into an energizing, satisfying and joyful experience. They witnessed my hard work, frequent suffering and occasional despair, which I did not expect them to mitigate. However, sometimes they did – thank you both! José, my promotor, allowed me time to find my way at first. Her monitoring of the writing process later on showed the same confidence and involvement, for which I am very grateful. Bernike, my co-promotor, sometimes made me insecure, challenging me to make up my mind, articulate my thoughts and express my ideas. I appreciated it just as much. José and Bernike, I think we made a good team!

Robert Zwijnenberg directed the NWO-funded research program The Mediated Body that included my project. It has been great to be one of the Bodies. I thank Rob for his inspiring leadership and him and the other Body-parts – Renée van de Vall, Jo Wachelder, Jenny Slatman, Rina Knoeff, Mieneke te Hennepe and associates Babette Müller-Rockstroh and Miriam van Rijsingen – for their invaluable contributions and for their intellectual and personal company during our research meetings and beyond.

The Mediated Body exemplified the interdisciplinarity of the Faculty of Arts and Culture at Maastricht University, where it was based. It was the best place to be. I particularly thank my fellow members of the department of Technology and Society Studies and the BOTS research colloquium, lead by Wiebe Bijker – an exemplary boss. My work has definitely benefited from comments on my work-in-progress provided by Rein de Wilde, Jessica Mesman, Margaret Meredith and from discussions with Marjolein van Asselt, Ruud Hendriks and many other colleagues, including the participants in the 'AiO-soep': Sophie,

Susan, Nikki, Julia, Merel, Vivian, Ludo, Martijn, Maaike, Alissa, Thijs, Patrick, Saskia, Cornelia, Leen, Leentje and Serge.

My PhD training in the WTMC research school presented a definite and recurring highlight, thanks to coordinators, teachers and participants. I thank Frank Veraart for the suggestion to call my my work *endography*, during one of the WTMC workshops. During a Summer School I met Sabina Leonelli and Martijn Wit. Together we were involved in establishing the Graduate Journal of Social Science. I have enjoyed the cooperation, company and friendship of the members of the GJSS editorial board: Sabina, Martijn, Ward Rennen, Wouter-Jan Oosten, Iris van der Tuin, André van Dokkum and Marcel Scheele.

In the early stages of my project, I joined a group of 'tinkerers': young researchers doing qualitative research in the field of health care. We only met a few times, yet this book shows the impact of our interactions, in particular those with Rita Struhkamp, Jeannette Pols and Teun Zuiderent.

As a newcomer to science and technology studies, I was pleasantly surprised to find so many Dutch sources of inspiration with international appeal. Nevertheless, crossing national borders – on-line and in real-life – made me part of an international research community, which has greatly benefited my work. I thank everyone who has left their traces during and following the international conferences and meetings that I have attended.

Eddy Houwaert of the Metamedica department at the Vrije Universiteit Amsterdam persisted in advocating a research career, which ultimately brought me to Maastricht. It was just what I needed at the time, and I thank him for that. When I announced my move to Sjaak van der Geest and Els van Dongen at the Medical Anthropology department of the University of Amsterdam, they feared I would be lost for medical anthropology. I hope I am still in: you have initiated and enforced my enduring fascination with health and illness, and the critical attitude that fostered the development of novel ways to understand them.

I left Maastricht before I finished this book. The Centre for the Society and Genomics, where I work now, has been a great support in the last phase. I especially thank Annemiek Nelis, who decided that I just had to finish it now, and made it possible. Hosts, guests and history of Kasteel Slangenburg provided just the right atmosphere to put on the final spurt.

I thank Nienke Wijnia, my friend since childhood who lives far but is always close, for her valuable last-minute editorial work.

Babette and Mieneke, my fellow musketeers. We shared the proverbial peaks and lows. It is amazing how we have managed to finish our books just within a few weeks from each other! I am grateful to have shared this experience with you. Mieneke, a special word to you: my roommate, friend, surrogate sister. I do not need to tell you how much I got from working with you and being with you. Thank you for being at my side as my paranimf.

My other paranimf is Hester, my real sister. Doing a PhD is only one among the many experiences that we have shared. I am happy with you next to me and I look forward to many more adventures together.

Riet and Gert, my parents, do not feel that they have contributed much to this endeavor. Yet besides contributing me, they have been an invaluable source of support for me and my family, together with their partners Jan and Marianne. Ontzettend bedankt, al weten jullie dan zogenaamd niet waarvoor.

Mats and Jochem could not believe it took me so long to write a single book, and not even such a big one. They put things into perspective and ensured that there was life outside the PhD. Ik verheug me erop nog heel veel met en van jullie te blijven leren en genieten!

Michel has always been there, for better and for worse. Dankjewel, voor veel meer dan ik hier kan zeggen.

Table of contents

1 Introduction: real-time medical imaging and the mediation of illness   1

Into the field   3

Performative endography   4

Transparency and alienation   5

Techno-visual mediations of embodied illness experience   6

Outlining patients and pictures   8

2 Patients in practice: exploring ways to talk about bodies   11

Interpreting illness: notions from anthropology and sociology   12

Embodiment and perception: phenomenological vocabularies   17

Bodily translations: vocabularies from science and technology studies   24

"Bodies in technology": post-phenomenological vocabularies   30

Conceptual confrontations   35

3 Patient compositions: preparing bodies for real-time imaging   41

Bodies in machines   42
Moving x-ray pictures: fluoroscopic spectacles and spectators   42
Seeing with sound   44
Interior inspections: endoscopic views inside the body   46
Machine-body interactions   48

Professional preparations   49
Learning by doing: haptic skills in real-time imaging   52

Patient preparations   54
Preparing one's body   55
Collecting information   57

Paper work: request forms as coordination devices   60
Bodies in categories   62
Translation, multiplication, coordination: the work of request forms   65

Collective embodiment and the enactment of disease and illness   66

4 Moving pictures: productions of presence in real-time imaging events   69

Of bodies and images in real-time   70
Mr. Coenen's ultrasonic kidneys   70
A fluoroscopic view of Mrs. Vermeulen's bladder   72
Endoscopic inspections of Mrs. den Hartog's large intestine   74
Momentary compositions   77

Image-body attachments 79
Real-time readings 80
Seeing one's own interior 86
Active dispossession 90
Moved by pictures 91
Images of bodies 92

Productions of presence 94

Real-time presence and illness experience 98

5   After the pictures: the embodiment of real-time medical images 101

Translation trajectories 102
From images to reports 103
From reports to patients 109
From screens to lived bodies 112
Translations of illness and disease 114

Image incorporations 115
The medical body 117
The transparent body 119
The spectacular body 121
Introspections: images of one's own body 123
From image to body 126

Illness in practice 130

6   Inside out: endographic conclusions 133

The circulation of illness 133

Myths on trial 134

The chain of real-time imaging 135

Interdisciplinary reflections 136

Distributed embodiment 137

Real-time imaging, articulate patients and the logic of care 139

Reflexivity in practice 142

References 145

Summary 151

Nederlandse samenvatting 159

Curriculum Vitae 167

1 Introduction: real-time medical imaging and the mediation of illness

(…) two masked men in surgical outfits look at the screen of a portable scanner. The senior doctor explains and demonstrates rapidly to his apprentice, the probe searching around the right side under the ribs and over the stomach, in sweeping motions. The intern listens raptly, nodding repeatedly. The screen is turned so that the patient can also see it. (….)

I emerged from surgery with the liver of an unknown five days ago. My attention now shifts to the two men as they speak, I follow their conversation and wait expectantly for words directed to me. It is a crucial moment: if the veins and arteries have not taken to their new place, my whole adventure comes to a halt. The graft, from their point of view, represents hardly anything more than a successful fixture. I am short of breath as I pick up the doctor's overheard telegraphic comments: Good portal circulation, no inflammation.... Abruptly he smiles to me and says: 'Tout va bien!' I am now my prostrate body that feels broken up, in bits and pieces, aching from a visible incision that goes from right to left in an arching path, and suddenly bifurcates over the chest right to my sternum, almost immobile from the multiple intubations and perfusions. His reassuring statement oddly makes me feel my liver as a small sphere, as if I am carrying an infant (I remember the pictures of my last son's beating heart in his mother's belly); it is tinged with a light pain, it is definitely present.

In the background, the brokenness of my body beckons me with an infinite fatigue, and a primordial desire to close my eyes and rest for eternity. Yet the screen is a few centimeters away and a simultaneous curiosity perks up unflinchingly. I can see my new liver, inside me. I follow the details: the anastomoses of the cava and the porta veins, the two large hepatic arteries, the II then the III lobule squished one into the other. I travel within, gliding inside and out of the liver capsule, like an animation. I listen with unabashed interest to the explanations to the intern (….).

We are looking at the scene from the side, you and I. And yet for me alone is echoed in multiple mirrors of shifting centres each of which I call 'I', each one a subject which feels and suffers, which expects a word, which is redoubled in a scanner's image, a concrete fragment that seems to partake with me of a mixture of intimacy and foreignness.

(Varela 2001: 259-60)

In a phenomenological account of his own liver transplantation with the telling title *Intimate distances* from which I quote here, neuroscientist and philosopher Francisco Varela describes an ultrasound examination performed five days after the surgery. Shifting from third person to first person to second person perspective, Varela pictures the experience. He describes the doctors moving the ultrasound transducer over the patient's abdomen, looking at the monitor and talking about what they see. He portrays himself – the patient – anxiously listening to their comments, sensing his body, watching strange yet familiar moving pictures on a monitor. He also depicts the author and the reader observing the scene.

This book is about experiences like the one so probingly described in this quote. It presents an analysis of how real-time medical imaging affects experiences of illness. The medical imaging technologies presented in this book share a particular quality that evokes that issue: they provide people with the fascinating possibility to look into one's own living body. The images of parts of patients' interior bodies produced by means of such visualization devices appear on a monitor before the eyes of both doctors and patients in real-time, immediately upon their acquisition. In this book I show how the particular ways of producing medical knowledge in clinical practices of real-time medical imaging bring along particular modes of embodiment and illness.

In today's medicine images are omnipresent. Before the introduction of X-rays in clinical medicine in 1896, the interior living human body was largely invisible. Anatomical images depicted inner bodies modeled after corpses. Medical imaging technologies like X-ray, CT, MRI, ultrasound and endoscopy provide visual access to the interior of a living human body without cutting the skin. These technologies produce different types of visual representations of the inner human body that can inform professional readers about the medical condition of that body. Although some expect that the possibilities of genetic diagnostics will cause the visualization of the living interior body to become less urgent in the future (cf. Houwaart and Kruisinga 2001: 251), at present the quantity of pictures made and the amount of money spent on medical imaging is growing rapidly (Van Engelshoven 2002).

Ultrasound, fluoroscopy and endoscopy are the imaging technologies that feature in this book. The three means of medical visualization all produce real-time moving images, yet they are substantially different as well. Ultrasound and fluoroscopy are radiological techniques used to produce dynamic streaming images of interior body structures and functions by means of sound waves and X-rays respectively. Their main objectives are diagnostic, although they can also be used to guide therapeutic interventions. Endoscopy amounts to surgical navigation by means of a video camera in a tube inserted in a bodily cavity.

To find out how real-time imaging transforms medical knowledge and embodied experience of illness, I went to a Dutch hospital and over a period of six months I spent most of my working days in the Radiology and Endoscopy departments. As a medical anthropologist, I had been trained in empirical observations of cultures of medicine, health and illness (cf. Radstake 2000). In the hospital I did what anthropologists do: fieldwork, participant observation, ethnography. However, this book is not the ethnography that anthropologists usually *write*. I have called it an *endography* which is a rather unusual term, occasionally used in medical settings to describe the technique of endoscopic ultrasound. I call this book an endography for three reasons. First, my fieldwork took place in my own habitat. Such 'anthropology at home' has been described as endo-ethnography (Van Ginkel 1998). [1] The second reason is the more significant one. Besides entering hospital departments, examination rooms and doctors' and patients' lives, I entered patients' bodies. Not only did I observe patients looking at their own interior, but I also watched the moving pictures of their insides, in real-time during an examination. A final reason why it seems appropriate to call this book an endography is the role of ethnographic material. My empirical observations and descriptions are starting points and benchmarks for an empirical-philosophical analysis of techno-visual mediations of embodied illness experience. Rather than interpretations of an outside reality, this book presents constructions of interiority.

Into the field

For a period of six months I spent several days a week in the Radiology and Endoscopy departments of a Dutch academic hospital. I watched doctors, nurses, assistants and technicians do their jobs and talked to them. I observed over forty real-time imaging events and interviewed patients afterwards. I copied preliminary and final reports and collected stored images. After they got the results, I called patients on the phone. Sometimes I joint them for follow-up with their physicians. I drew maps of the technical set-up of various examinations and read manuals and protocols. The hospital's medical-ethical committee allowed me to talk to patients after they had given their consent on the basis of written information about my project. I could only approach patients upon check-in at the reception desk in the radiology or endoscopy department. In-patients were therefore excluded from my study. I also excluded patients who checked in for an examination that did not meet my criteria, i.e. being an ultrasound, fluoroscopic or endoscopic examination of the abdomen resulting in pictures that could be watched by the patient. Furthermore, some of the patients checking in were so sick, so uneasy, or so upset that I did not approach them. Of the people I approached, one in four did not want to participate. Yet a considerable number of people accepted my presence during a sometimes unpleasant and embarrassing examination.

---

[1] The classical Greek prefix 'endo-' means 'inside' or 'interior'.

Ultrasound, fluoroscopy and endoscopy are used for the inspection of various body parts. Ultrasound is best known for its obstetric use, but it is also used to visualize the abdomen, kidneys, heart, testicles or leg arteries.[2] Stomachs, intestines, uteri and bladders, but also knee joints can be inspected endoscopically. Fluoroscopy is used to visualize the movement of contrast fluids in arteries, ovaries, bowels and urinary tracts. From the wide range of examinations I made a selection based on two criteria related to my research question. First, I only included examinations during which patients were physically able to watch the monitor during the examination. They were conscious or only lightly sedated; they were positioned in such a way that the monitor was in visual reach at least during part of the examination; and they were not too ill to watch. Secondly, I wanted to observe visualizations of the most 'bodily' of body parts in order to take the materialities of embodiment seriously. Whereas in contemporary western culture and medicine the heart represents life and the brain accommodates the mind, the organs of the abdomen denote little more than their physical functions and location.[3] Body parts are treated differentially (Young 1989: 45), also by anthropologists, sociologists and philosophers writing about bodies and embodiment. I have taken the opportunity to descend into the depths of the 'absent body' (Leder 1990), a concept that I will discuss in the next chapter.

Performative endography

The methods of ethnography – and of endography in its wake – fit both the empirical and the theoretical setting of my project. I lacked essential conditions, skills and perceptions for true participant observation of real-time imaging practices from either a physician's or a patient's point of view. Yet being there, combining verbal with non-verbal interactions and with observations of behavior, allowed me to move beyond people's interpretations of reality, into their ways of doing. That made it possible "to reconstruct the world not through a grid of

---

[2] The ethical and political implications of the use of ultrasound in pregnancy have been amply and aptly analysed by various scholars from different disciplines (Duden 1993a, Mitchell 2001, Mueller-Rockstroh 2007, Petchesky 1987, Price 1996, Rapp 1997, Stabile 1998, Taylor 1998). I leave it out for two other reasons as well. First, obstetric ultrasound involves the depiction of at least two bodies, that of the mother and that of the fetus, with the latter in visual focus. My focus is on the impact of watching pictures of unknown part of one's own body. Secondly, I am interested in mediations of illness. Most pregnancies luckily do not fall into that category, although critics of the ongoing medicalization of conception, pregnancy and birth have argued that it is increasingly made to do so (e.g. Barker 1998, Smeenk and Ten Have 2003).

[3] In other cultural contexts different modes of ordering may be found. Cashinahua people in Peru, for example, locate emotional knowledge in the liver and social knowledge in the ears and do not consider the brain as a central locus in any way different from the rest of the body (cf. Jackson 1996: 34).

attributed meanings, but through a series of interventions carried out – which allows (me, MR) to talk about realities that are transformed" (Mol 1998: 145). In the next chapter I will introduce actor-network theory as one of my main sources for theoretical inspiration. Its method has been heavily influenced by the ethno-methodological idea that in order to understand what actors do and why and how they do it, you have to learn from the actors themselves. Anthropologists advocating performative (or dialogical) ethnography have argued that the only way to do this is by acknowledging that you yourself are an actor in whatever it is you study (e.g. Fabian 1991, Pool 1994). Although I do not explicitly address this issue throughout this book, I have entered the field in the awareness that "the Other is never simply given, never just found or encountered, but made" (Fabian 1991: 208). Rather than learning from the actors in the field of real-time medical imaging, I have been learning with them. My presence transformed the practices I observed. Some patients sought my eyes during an examination, looking for assurance or support. Although some liked to have me around, others were embarrassed. Several doctors and assistants reported to adjust their behavior when I was around, especially by giving more explanations to the patient or by explicitly addressing me. The real-time imaging practices that I studied included my own performance as a researcher.

Transparency and alienation

Real-time imaging technologies provide both physicians and patients with a seemingly direct, unmediated view inside a living body. Even more than other medical technologies, real-time imaging contributes to the popular utopic discourse of a transparent body that is readily accessible, controllable and manipulable (cf. Van Dijck 2005). When three-dimensional (3D) ultrasound entered clinical practices in the 1990s there was "a kind of manic exhilaration over the epistemic earnings potential of this virtual reality tour of the body (....) the images are so "life-like" that they seduce the viewer into thinking that the representation of the object is isomorphic with the object itself; the images seems to be just like what would be seen with our own eyes, but even better (....)" (Barad 1998: 118). 3D ultrasound images are not discussed in this book. Endoscopic images, however, have similar life-like qualities and the real-time visual accessibility of 2D ultrasound and fluoroscopic images gives them a comparable seductive power and evoke the image of a transparent body. Paradoxically, medical professionals generally consider real-time images to be relatively unreliable, 'subjective' representations of bodily realities, because they can only be interpreted by the ones who produce them. To conclude that the idea of a transparent body merely reflects patients' unrealistic expectations, as I heard several physicians do, is, however, premature. Throughout the book I will argue that a 'transparent body' is actively being evoked as well as challenged in real-time imaging practices.

A more dystopic discourse on medical technology is the trope of disembodiment or alienation found in phenomenological literature and in social-scientific work inspired by phenomenology (see Akrich and Pasveer 2004, Duden 1993b, Good 1994, Ihde 2002, Leder 1990, Stacey 1998, Toombs 1992, Young 1997). It is the idea that medical objectivations and technological representations move away human bodies from embodied selves and thus enforce the alienating effect of being ill. Put briefly, medical images show everything but one's own body. This way of thinking can also be found in biomedicine itself. In his inaugural speech at the University of Groningen in 2002, Dutch radiology professor Matthijs Oudkerk stated that since Vesalius and Harvey medicine has reduced human bodies to images, ultimately culminating in the rise of radiology. Radiology has enforced the alienation of the body, Oudkerk claimed (Oudkerk 2002). It has also been claimed, however, that an increase of technology in medical practice results in 'more talk', that is more attention for the patient as person (Mol 2001). Radiology can only be described as a technology that alienates patients from their bodies if one presupposes that representations of a body essentially differ from 'lived bodies'. In this book I doubt this essential difference. Not only are "vision, visuality and visibility (...) as central to the subjective dimensions of embodied existence as they are to its objective dimensions" (Sobchack 2004: 2): subjective and objective dimensions shape each other in visualization practices. A disembodiment or alienation discourse opposes so-called objective medical and technological representations of the human body to subjective embodied experience. I will argue that real-time imaging challenges this opposition: bodies cannot self-evidently be distinguished from their images.

Techno-visual mediations of embodied illness experience

In this book I examine co-productions of images and illness (cf. Pasveer 1994), elaborating the proposition that far from simply depicting given bodies, medical images *mediate* bodily realities. What I mean by that is that the reference of images to the medical condition of human bodies is the result of particular historical, institutional, professional and cultural practices in which imaging technologies have developed and are being used. People's relations with reality can be described in different philosophical terms. In epistemological terms, people relate to the world as an object of *knowledge*. Phenomenologists describe the *experience* of 'being-in-the-world'.[4] The distinction between knowledge and experience is reflected in the social-scientific difference between *disease* as the object of professional medical knowledge and *illness* as a socio-cultural and personal experience, which I will discuss in chapter 2.

While describing the subsequent stages of preparation, image production, and interpretation, I analyze how knowledge and experience, disease and illness are transformed and co-constructed in practices of real-time medical imaging. When radiologists or other imaging professionals 'read' medical images, they do not decode implicit meanings, as historians of medical imaging have assumed (cf. Holtzmann-Kevles 1997). Rather, they create material and discursive links between images and bodies. For patients, being sick or healthy is part of their embodied 'being-in-the-world'. Medical images mediate patients' experience of their own bodies. Real-time imaging is a particularly convenient practice to study relations between medical knowledge and embodied experiences of illness and health. The moving pictures shown on a monitor during a real-time imaging event refer to a body that is both the object of medical examination as well as the object *and* the subject of a patient's sensory perception and agency. Because of its characteristic simultaneous mediation of professional knowledge production and of patients' embodied experience, real-time medical imaging begs for any subject-object distinction to be bypassed. My focus is therefore on how patient bodies are *done* in practice (cf. Mol and Law 2004: 45). Rather than asking what images mean, I ask what real-time imaging does to illness and embodiment.

Understanding how real-time medical imaging affects experiences of illness calls for a concept of illness that is more sophisticated than the notion that has been developed and used in medical anthropology and sociology. Throughout this book I develop a concept of illness that makes it possible to describe and understand its multiple layers and their interrelations.

---

[4] A phenomenological term to describe human existence. The phenomenological frame and vocabulary will be further explored in chapter 2.

Outlining patients and pictures

Francisco Varela's moving account of an experience of real-time imaging is situated in a place where the leading question for this book originates and where most of my fieldwork started: in the examination room during a real-time imaging event. Readers who are eager to share the initial fascination and puzzlement I felt, should start reading chapter 4 before looking at other chapters. However, although starting *in medias res* would be in line with the method of actor-network theory that has strongly directed my work, I have decided that both the accessibility of the field and the understandability of my theoretical argument benefit from a more chronological set-up. The chapters address subsequent stages in the trajectories of patients going through real-time imaging and in the trajectories of the images that are produced.

Chapter 2 contains short field fragments describing how people became patients in the first place. However, it mainly explores the conceptual frames of the anthropology and sociology of health and medicine, (post-)phenomenology and actor-network theory to collect building blocks for my analysis of illness as a technologically mediated, layered experience in the subsequent chapters.

The second stage of an imaging trajectory, described in chapter 3, consists of the preparations of imaging devices, physicians, forms and protocols and by patients themselves, transforming patients into bodies that are ready for real-time imaging. Chapter 3 is engrafted onto actor-network theory and presents the individual and joint preparations of human and non-human actors for real-time imaging as a process of collective embodiment. Patients' bodies and medical conditions result from such preparations, rather than precede them. This applies to bodies as (material) objects of examination and visualization as well as to their agency and identity. Objectivation and subjectivation are tied together from the beginning. Actor-network theory can be used to describe both, but will this be sufficient to understand the production of experience?

In chapter 4 that presents the actual imaging event, I argue that more is needed to address the realm of actual experience in the case of real-time imaging. An analysis of how medical data and bodily sensations emerge as potential referents of real-time images during their actual production further blurs the boundaries between knowledge and experience. During a real-time imaging event, the patient's body is – simultaneously and temporarily – present on the examination table and on the monitor, as a visual and tactile object and as a spectator. Material, discursive, agential and emotional attachments of bodies and images produce an embodied mode of presence that conditions further translations of real-time imaging events.

Such further translations of a body's real-time presence during a real-time imaging event are described in chapter 5. In this chapter we follow images rather than bodies. It describes two interconnected follow-up trajectories: how imaging events contribute to medical knowledge production and how they are translated into narratives, body images and other expressions of embodied experience. Immediately after a real-time imaging event there are images, perceptions, interpretations and experiences, yet there is no diagnosis yet, nor do patients have a coherent narrative about the relation between the images and their own body. The last stage in my analysis describes how professional and patients' translations of bodily presences result in embodied experiences of health and illness. Health or illness are neither the outcome of processes of signification, nor inherent qualities of bodies. Illness is a matter of practice. Real-time imaging mediates health and illness as embodied experiences by affecting various ways in which bodies are made to appear. I conclude the book with some reflections on the theoretical, practical and political relevance and implications of my analysis.

Patients in practice: exploring ways to talk about bodies

While observing examinations in a radiology and in an endoscopy department to study how real-time imaging affects the bodies of patients, I saw many different bodies: male, female, young, old, sick, aching, silent, hungry or active bodies, bodies on the examination table and bodies on the monitor. Those were the bodies of people, embodied human beings with divergent histories and conditions, who all ended up on an examination table, looking at a monitor that showed pictures of their interior. In this book I describe how patients travel from their home via a general practitioner or another physician to an examination room in the radiology or endoscopy department and back. Along the way patients' bodies get linked to real-time, moving images of parts of their body. When being processed by physicians, patients, and technological devices, pictures become clinical representations of a patient's medical condition as well as objects of his or her own reflections. Practices of real-time imaging are extraordinary, for they grant patients a visual experience of their own interior body. In medical settings, where real-time imaging events usually take place, health or illness are the issues at stake: as objects of visualization and diagnosis as well as experiences of living bodies. I present an analysis of the bodily transformations that the travels of bodies and images entail and 'ways to talk about bodies'[5]: a method and vocabulary to describe the production of embodied experiences of health and illness related to such transformations.

The set-up of the current chapter reflects the heuristics of my empirical-philosophical project.[6] I carried out fieldwork in radiology and endoscopy departments to find out which exactly were the questions I wanted to address. I turned to four bodies of philosophical and social-scientific work for directions on how to tackle the issue of real-time medical imaging and illness experience. The four core sections of the current chapter each introduce concepts and ideas from a particular theoretical vocabulary: interpretative *medical anthropology* and *sociology of health and illness*, *phenomenology*, *actor-network theory* and a synthesis of the latter two that has been labeled *post-phenomenology* (Verbeek 2005). These four frames are central because their respective focus is on the central elements that constitute my question:

---

[5] Cf. Latour 2004.
[6] Cognate to empirical philosophy as practiced and described by Annemarie Mol (Mol 2002).

illness in medical anthropology, *embodied experience* in phenomenology, *technological mediation* in actor-network theory and a confrontation between the latter two in post-phenomenology.

Case stories have more or less arbitrarily been assigned to each section. They illustrate the first step in the transformation of bodies into images: how people become patients. An in-depth analysis of this phase - which includes falling ill, looking for causes and solutions, seeing a doctor and being referred for further examination - falls outside the scope of this book. The case stories in this chapter indicate what patients have experienced and done before they ended up on an examination table for an endoscopic, fluoroscopic or ultrasound examination. Each of the four theoretical frameworks or vocabularies addresses and evokes different questions and different ways to analyze a case story. The juxtaposition of empirical cases and conceptual explorations in this chapter reflects my constant going back and forth between field notes and literature. The eventual results of that interaction will be presented throughout the book.

Anthropology, actor-network theory and (post-)phenomenology involve different questions, different epistemologies and different ontologies. Combining such diverging frames is not self-evident. Relating them to the specific practice of real-time medical imaging evokes both a theoretically challenging confrontation as well as a new understanding of a fascinating practice. While exploring promising concepts and vocabularies in this chapter, I collect building blocks for a framework particularly suited to describe and understand how experiences of health and illness come about in clinical practices of real-time medical imaging. I develop that framework in the book. In the present chapter I work the soil and sow the seeds.

Interpreting illness: notions from anthropology and sociology

68-year-old Mr. Bergmans[7] has regularly suffered from abdominal pain over the past years. We talk after a fluoroscopic examination of his colon in the radiology department.[8]

---

[7] All names of patients are pseudonyms.

[8] The case stories in this chapter are based on various sources: patients' medical files, my observations of interactions among doctors and between doctors and patients during and after examinations, and my conversations with patients after an examination. I do not consider them as documents – factual accounts of what has actually happened – but rather as performative instruments, (re-)constructing the course of events.

MR   Now what was this examination for? You had abdominal pains?

MB   Abdominal pains, right, I had abdominal pains. I recently had that. It surely has been more than three years that I have eaten yogurt with cereal for lunch. And then one day, I did not do that, I ate a sandwich for lunch, and then I did not have a bellyache. And I thought: now that is strange. Then I stopped the yogurt. And then I did not have the stomach-ache anymore, it was gone. Only pain here, in the groin. Well... But what it was? I cannot imagine that it was because of yogurt. But my bellyache was gone.

MR   The doctor had no clue?

MB   No, I had been to my general practitioner already, for the bellyache. That was about a month ago. Then I came here, early January. And I had to wait until today, January 30th.

MR   But you did not have symptoms anymore?

MB   No, no symptoms. I did not have pain anymore.

(…)

MR   That stomach-ache, how long did you have that?

MB   About two months.

MR   And did you have any idea what it could be?

MB   No.

MR   Did you think it were your bowels?

MB   I immediately thought of cancer, that is what I thought of at first.

MR   Why? Why did you think of that?

MB   You hear it from many people: examinations, and that after a month it turns out to be cancer. I was somewhat afraid of that.

MR   Did the family doctor tell you anything, about what he thought it might be?

MB   No, he had no idea. He pushed on my belly everywhere. That is all he can do, isn't it? He cannot see it.

MR   Since he does not have all those machines?

MB   Right. So he referred me right away. I do not often visit the GP, so he knows that if I come, it must be serious.

MR   You were really worried.

MB   Yes, I was.

MR   And when the pain was gone, were you less worried?

MB   A bit. But I am not at ease about it.

MR   And you hope to find out more with this examination?

MB   Yes, I do.

In the above fragment Mr. Bergmans describes the onset of his recent illness, what he thinks possibly caused it and how he went about looking for a diagnosis and treatment for his problem. Medical anthropologists[9] have called such a set of notions about a particular episode of sickness an *explanatory model* (Kleinman 1980: 104 ff.). Mr. Bergmans presents his explanatory model as an illness narrative: a story about falling and being ill and looking for treatment. His story reveals particular features of the context in which this explanatory model is employed: cancer is a well-known and dreaded disease and medical imaging technologies seem to be valued over a physical examination to locate the cause of illness inside the body. According to Mr. Bergmans, medical images can show a doctor what cannot be felt or otherwise known. Had it not been for my interest in medical imaging, Mr. Bergmans might not have explicitly mentioned it in his account. When I asked him about the examination he told me about symptoms, worries and expectations: he expressed his illness experience. The examination was one among other ingredients of that experience.

The fluoroscopic examination contributed to the translation of Mr. Bergmans' illness into a disease. To readers whose native language is not English and to those unfamiliar with medical anthropology, the distinction between illness and disease may not be obvious.[10] It is a central distinction in interpretative medical anthropology (e.g. Eisenberg 1977; Kleinman 1980, 1988; Helman 2001). Where *illness* is used to denote a *person's* psychosocial and cultural experience, perception and interpretation of *being* ill, *disease* refers to physical or mental abnormalities in the structure and function of a body. Disease is a condition one *has*. Whereas illness is something human - only humans are capable of social, lived experience, recognition of symptoms and seeking treatment - disease is a technical failure or biological abnormality that can also be diagnosed in plants or animals (Lupton 2003: 93-4). In other words, illness is what a patient *feels* when going to the doctor, whereas disease is what the doctor *diagnoses* (Helman 2001: 83).

Medical anthropologists do not study disease as a physical condition – as doctors do –, but as the object of biomedical diagnosis and treatment. They characterize medical professional ways of dealing with disease by its scientific rationality, its emphasis on objective, numerical measurements as well as on physicochemical data, its mind-body dualism, its view of diseases as entities, its reductionism, and its emphasis on the individual

---

[9]'Medical anthropologists' refers to cultural anthropologists with a particular interest in health, illness and medicine as socio-cultural phenomena in their own or in other societies. Although the interpretative approach has become mainstream in contemporary medical anthropology, the field also includes scholars who work from a different perspective. Broadly speaking, two major approaches can be identified in medical anthropology. The first builds on techniques and findings from medical science (e.g. genetics, epidemiology, nutrition) and attempts primarily to describe and explain relations between biological changes and social and cultural factors in a particular society. At the other end of the spectrum is the interpretative ethnographic approach that I relate to here.

[10] In Dutch, the word 'ziekte' would be used for both terms.

patient body (Helman 2001: 79). Anthropologists study the explanatory models of medical professionals about disease as well as the lay explanatory models, which are about illness. Illness denotes one's own and others' interpretations and actions evoked by being unwell. Illness is not "a subjective phenomenon – something that a single person 'has'- but an interpersonal medium shared by, engaged in and also mediating between persons in a local world" (Kleinman and Kleinman 1998: 213). Anthropologists look at the context of lay explanations as well as medical professional explanatory models (Helman 2001: 86).[11]

Anthropologists usually study illness experience by interpreting its expressions (cf. Kleinman 1988; Good 1994: 135 ff.; Hydén 1997; Mattingly & Garro 2000). Experience can be expressed in words but also in behavior or images. Interpretative anthropologists take the relation between experience and expression to be dialogic and dialectical: they structure each other (Bruner 1986: 5-6). Expressions are not merely representations of experience, but they disclose experience (Csordas 1999: 146). In their observations of and conversations with people, most anthropologists primarily collect, evoke and co-produce stories that articulate events and discuss and construct meanings. In studying illness narratives, the experience of illness and embodiment can be studied as "a social and cultural construct, as a transformation and expression of bodily suffering, and most of all as the suffering person's attempt to construct his or her world, to find his or her own life-work and life-context"(Hydén 1997: 65).

Disease and illness, expressed narratively and discursively, are embedded in the physical materiality of human bodies. An exemplary medical anthropological conceptualization of embodiment has been developed by cultural anthropologists Nancy Scheper-Hughes and Margaret Lock. Their 'mindful body' includes the individual body, or the lived experience of the body-self; the social body, which is symbolically used to represent nature, society and culture; and the body-politic – controlled, regulated and surveyed by political institutions (Scheper-Hughes and Lock 1998 (1987)). Such a concept of embodiment fits rather well with the concerns of 'critical medical anthropology', in which the body is understood "both as a product of biology and of social and cultural processes; simultaneously totally biological and totally cultural" (Guarnaccia in Lupton 2003: 16). The ways in which people understand their bodies, and the ways in which they understand their society, are interconnected and mutually shaping (cf. Isenberg and Owen in Young 1989: 44).

---

[11] Arthur and Joan Kleinman have warned against the risk of culturalization that comes with such a contextual focus. Anthropologists should be aware that their professional discourse can be just as dehumanizing as medical or psychological counterparts, since a description of illness experience in terms of culture transforms it as much as (medical) descriptions in terms of nature do (Kleinman and Kleinman 1998: 199-200). What medical anthropologists need to do is find out what is at stake for various participants in particular practices (Kleinman and Kleinman: 213).

Interpretative medical anthropology shares many questions, concepts and themes with contemporary sociology of health and illness. Despite their different disciplinary backgrounds, the two sub-disciplines have developed a common social-constructivist approach. Social constructivism also covers large parts of history, cultural studies and feminist research on health, illness and medicine. Inspired by the work of Michel Foucault, social constructivist concepts of the body are largely framed in terms of its discursive constitution and discipline and its role in framing human subjectivity (Lupton 2003: 12-13). In a social-constructivist framework, knowledge production implies the construction of reality through practices, and it brings along particular subjectivities. The truth claims of biomedicine as well as the reality of illness and other embodied experiences emerge from social and cultural practices of knowledge production and interpretation.

The story of Mr. Bergmans shows how the transformation of a patient's body into an object of medical visualization brings along a transformation of the embodied subject as well. Mr. Bergmans no longer relies on his own physical sensations to know whether or not he is healthy, but needs a physician to virtually open up his body and look inside. Medical anthropologists have hardly explicitly addressed the main issue in this book: how people's relations with (medical) technologies shape embodied experience. Anthropologist's Cecil Helman statement about technological mediations of people's images of the insides of their bodies is an exception:

> To most people the inner structure of the body is a matter of mystery and speculation. Without the benefit of anatomical dissections, charts of the skeletal or organ structures or X-ray photographs, beliefs about how the body is constructed are usually based on inherited folklore, books and magazines, personal experience and theorizing. The importance of this 'inside-the-body' image is that it influences people's perception and presentation of bodily complaints. It also influences their responses to medical treatment. (Helman 2001: 16)

The use of medical technologies has been described as part of the 'disease perspective' that reduces illness experience to a biomedical condition, yet also as altering "our sense of the human body" (Helman 2001: 65). My question about techno-visual mediations of illness emanates from the hypothesis that patients' illness experiences are mediated by biomedical constructions of their bodies as (possible) accommodations of disease. Medical anthropology and the sociology of health and illness offer a rich vocabulary to describe both professional and lay understandings and practices of health, illness and health care. However, their analyses maintain an essential distinction between disease as the object of medical knowledge, and illness as the object of lay experience. I argue that such a distinction is at odds with a study of illness as a mode of embodiment, for it implies a distinction between the patient as person (being ill) and as body (having a disease), that cannot empirically be substantiated in a context of technological mediation. In the next section I turn to phenomenology to address this problem and look for a vocabulary to describe experiences of embodied persons.

Embodiment and perception: phenomenological vocabularies

Mr. Theunissen is forty-nine years old and was diagnosed with inflammatory bowel disease after an endoscopic examination seventeen years ago. After a long period of relatively stable health, Mr. Theunissen's condition deteriorated five years ago. Endoscopies, biopsies and blood tests have resulted in various adjustments of treatment, but not in a lasting improvement. The attending gastroenterologist has performed yearly endoscopic check-ups over the past years.

The disease has seriously affected the life of Mr. Theunissen. Medication prescribed to fight the infection, for instance, interfered with his wife's and his desire to have children by means of infertility treatment. They do not have any children now. Mr. Theunissen has a job, but has been declared partly unfit to work because of his condition. The disease limits his personal freedom: a toilet must always be within reach. Leaving the house is therefore a problem. Mr. Theunissen takes medication to fight recurring depressions that he and the doctor both ascribe to his ill-health.

I talked to Mr. Theunissen after an endoscopic examination of his large intestine and asked him what has preceded the examination.

> MR   Did you feel that it (the condition of the intestines, MR) was not okay?
> MT   Yes, that is daily routine. In fact, it is always the same. I can feel that it is still the same.

More specifically about the examination, I asked Mr. Theunissen:

> MR   When you watch the pictures on the monitor, what does it mean to you?
> MT   One never knows whether it is good or bad. The doctor really has to say: this is not good, and that is okay. One knows, you yourself, you see it from the inside, but....
> MR   Yes, how are you supposed to know what it should look like?
> MT   There is no comparison, to what it should look like.

MR   You have had many examinations already, so maybe you could compare between them.

MT   That is right. But back then, it was impossible for me to watch the monitor, actually.[12]

(....)

MR   When you think back to when you first watched those images, did your body look different than you expected? Or did you not really have an image of it?

MT   I did not have an image. You know you have a gut, but what does it look like? You have seen pictures sometimes, but you have no idea of what it really looks like.

MR   And now you have, after several examinations?

MT   Yes, now I have an idea.

Mr. Theunissen describes how frequent biomedical interventions, including medical visualizations, have informed his perceptions of his own body and his illness. Not only has he learned to feel what condition his colon is in, he has also become acquainted with an endoscopic view of his intestines. An anthropological analysis could infer a confrontation of lay explanations – representing what a patient feels – and professional explanatory models based on doctors' accounts of what they see. An analysis in those terms would present Mr. Theunissen and his ill body as effects of contrasting cultural and biomedical constructions.

As I mentioned in the previous section, the implicit separation between person and body that corresponds with an anthropological illness and disease distinction, impedes an understanding of illness as a mode of embodiment. Because the distinction between 'disease' and 'illness' has not been challenged, illness has remained a subjective category separate from the realm of professional and technological objectivation. A number of anthropologists and sociologists have turned to phenomenology in order to address the particular issue of embodiment as "the existential ground of culture and self" and thus "a paradigm for anthropology" (Csordas 1994, 1990). Interpretative anthropologists state that illness experiences concern patients' bodies as physical objects, but also affect their identities, their selves:

> Sickness and pain submit experience to the body's vital rhythms, infusing everyday experience with its distorting presence, focusing our awareness on the body as object, alien to the experiencing self, the object of cultural practices. (Good 1994: 131)

---

[12] Because of a different set-up for the examination, patients where thus positioned that they could not watch the monitor.

In line with Good and other anthropologists, sociologists have argued for "a more experientially grounded view of human embodiment as the existential basis of our being-in-the-world" (Williams and Bendelow 1998: 8).

The notion of 'being-in-the-world' has been introduced by Martin Heidegger. It can be traced back to the work of Edmund Husserl who founded *phenomenology* at the turn of the 19th to the 20th century as a method to conceptualize and describe human experience. Husserl's concept of experience included a variety of activities, givens and accomplishments that presuppose human consciousness: thinking, imagining, remembering, perceiving and willing, but also time-consciousness, intersubjectivity, the self, common sense and corporeality (Rogers 1983: 1). Since "human experience includes a sense of ourselves as subject and as objects" (Jackson 1996: 21), a phenomenological approach to experience addresses both modalities. Phenomenological experience, however, is not exclusively individual. Experience is intersubjective, i.e. it results from interactions between human beings. Moreover, phenomenologists consider subjectivity and objectivity as essentially different, but not opposed. They do not argue for a primacy of subjectivity in descriptions of human experience, but oppose to the reduction of experience to scientific, objective data.

Mr. Theunissen's experience includes both what he perceives – i.e. a part of his body - and how he perceives it by means of his physical senses. Human embodiment has been a central theme in the work of French philosopher Maurice Merleau-Ponty (1908-1961), especially elaborated in his *Phénomenologie de la perception* (1945). Like Husserl, Merleau-Ponty opposed the idea that human experience can be grasped in mathematical and physical terms (Jackson 1996: 30). Although people may sometimes experience themselves as disembodied or their bodies as objects, human experience in general cannot be reduced to quantitative, scientific facts (Jackson 1996: 31). The Cartesian division between mind and body, subject and object, impedes a description of the relation between consciousness and embodiment in terms of experience. Although a human body is never a thing, it is never bare consciousness either. Rather than an attribute of the human mind, which acts upon a physical object-body, subjectivity is a bodily being-in-the-world (Jackson 1996: 32). The body is the "very medium whereby our world comes into being" (Leder 1990: 5). Illness is a condition of a 'lived body', a notion introduced in phenomenology by Merleau-Ponty.

Whereas "the subject-object distinction is a product of analysis, and objects themselves are end results of perception rather than being given empirically to perception" (Csordas 1990: 9), the notion of a *lived body* points to the idea that experience "can only be understood between mind and body – or across them – in their lived conjunction" (Grosz

1994: 95). A body is both what people have and what they are. Embodiment is the condition for the objectivation of reality (cf. Csordas 1999: 183) as well as the ground for subjective perception. Elizabeth Grosz has emphasized that a shift from mind to body as the locus of subjectivity does not imply that notions such as agency and consciousness are redundant. She argues for a refiguration of subjective experience in corporeal rather than interior terms and for an understanding of the body as "the very 'stuff' of subjectivity" (Grosz 1994: ix). Grosz proposes a framework in which

> the body provides a point of mediation between what is perceived as purely internal and accessible only to the subject and what is external and publicly observable, a point from which to rethink the opposition between the inside and the outside, the private and the public, the self and the other, and all the other binary pairs associated with the mind/body opposition. (Grosz 1994: 21)

In such a framework Mr. Theunissen's multiple perceptions of his own interior body and illness can be described as a unitary process of embodiment rather than in terms of a dichotomy between professional and lay perceptions of bodies and selves. Anthropologist Thomas Csordas has drawn upon the phenomenology of Maurice Merleau-Ponty to argue that "culture does not reside only in objects and representations, but also in the bodily processes of perception by which those representations come into being" (Csordas 1999: 183). What people see, feel and otherwise experience – Csordas (1993) calls this 'somatic modes of attention'– follows from the culture they embody. One has to look at culture, which in most contemporary societies includes biomedical practices, in order to understand embodiment and to know that "(a) full understanding of any human body gives, at the same time, a fuller understanding of the culture embodied with it" (Helman 2001: 15).

Merleau-Ponty introduced the psycho-analytical concept of *body image* in phenomenology (cf. Weiss 1999: 34 ff.). Psycho-analysts like Sigmund Freud and especially Jacques Lacan emphasized the importance of body images for one's sense of self. Lacan argued that in the so-called 'mirror stage' - when an infant (between the age of 6 and 18 months) learns to identify with its image in a mirror by distinguishing its own body from its spatially removed image – the body image becomes an integrated part of one's body (Lacan 1953). In chapters 4 and 5 of this book I will argue that the experience of watching real-time medical images of one's interior body shows some similarities with seeing oneself in a mirror. The comparison is helpful in understanding the specific features of embodied experience in that particular techno-medical practice.

The concept of body image originated from neurology where it has served to explain neuro-pathological forms of body experience. It has been transferred to psychology where 'body image' has come to refer to the ways in which people conceptualize and experience the shape and size of their body, its boundaries, its inner structures and its functions. The psychological body image is an integrated part of one's body and consists of neurological, psychological and socio-cultural features: "the body image cannot be reduced to a physiological, psychological or purely social phenomenon, since it is the site where all three interact in a complex and dynamic fashion" (Weiss 1999: 162). Despite its visual and optical connotations, 'body image' refers to synesthetic experience, i.e. perception by all five senses. Body image is not only what people believe their body to look like, but also how they conceptualize its tactility, sound, taste and smell. The body image provides a unity that enables the senses to be translated into - or understood in terms of - other senses (Grosz 1994: 100).

Body images link people's perceptions of their own body and the bodies of others to their identity, sense of self and social relations. When a body or its condition changes, body images are adjusted. Although the basis of a stable embodied identity, body images are multiple, flexible and dynamic. For Mr. Theunissen, his abnormal medical state had become the normal experience of his body over the years. The illness has transformed his perceptions of his own body, but over the years, it has become part of his normal body, and of him as a person. What an examination shows, affects the body image of Mr. Theunissen. Mr. Theunissen has learned how to relate what he feels inside his body to what medical images show the doctor. The transformation of his body image evoked by medical visualization mediates how his body is present for Mr. Theunissen (cf. Grosz 1994: 62).

Phenomenologists have mostly written about images of the *exterior* body, as it can be seen in a mirror. Real-time imaging technologies produce images of the *interior* body. I have observed visualizations of parts of patients' digestive and urinary systems, like kidneys, livers, spleens, intestines, bladders, and gallbladders. For the most part, visceral phenomena[13] are unavailable to one's conscious awareness and control. They have largely been neglected in phenomenological accounts of embodiment. Where self perceptions of the exterior body are direct, visceral perception is largely indirect and requires mediation of some sort, often via the surface of the body.[14] American physician and philosopher Drew Leder has written a

---

[13] "The category of the "visceral" understood broadly includes not only the organs of the digestive system but of the respiratory, cardiovascular, urogenital, and endocrine systems, along with the spleen" (Leder 1990: 37).
[14] Although not explicitly about the role of skin in (self) perception, Te Hennepe's analysis of 19th century developments in scientific, medical and public depictions of skin offers an interesting background to think about these issues (Te Hennepe 2007).

phenomenology of 'the absent body' (Leder 1990). He has distinguished different ways in which the body can be absent from experience, including disappearance[15], invisibility and inaccessibility. One of the body's modes of absence is the recessive body. Leder describes the body as a field "in which certain organs and abilities come to prominence while others recede" (Leder 1990: 24). The organs of the interior body largely recede from conscious experience.

Leder discerns three categories of bodily perceptions: exteroception (perception of the surface body through one of the five senses), proprioception (the sense of balance, position and muscular tension) and interoception (sensations of the internal organs of the body) (Leder 1990: 39). Although one can increase one's awareness of visceral processes such as blood pulse, respiration or digestion by attending to them more closely, experiencing the interior body is largely an oblivious affair. The disappearance or absence of the interior body is reflected in the vocabulary used to describe visceral sensations, which is far less sophisticated than the language available to describe various perceptions through one or more of the five senses.[16] When I asked Mr. Theunissen, for example, how he felt whether the infection of his intestine was active, he told me that he 'just felt it' and referred to the presence of red and white spots on the endoscopic pictures to explain how serious it was.

I share with Leder the intuition that in order to understand embodiment, analyses of the 'higher' and what Leder has called 'ecstatic' regions of the corporeal field should be complemented by descriptions of bodies "fully fleshed out with bone and guts" (Leder 1990: 36). The 'interior introspection' made possible by real-time medical imaging technologies offers an opportunity to provide such complementary accounts and to include the absent body in body images.

Another mode of bodily absence that Leder describes is the *dys*-appearing body, when the body is a problematic or disharmonious thing and is therefore experienced as "being away"(Leder 1990: 70). Illness is one of the forces which may disrupt the temporary equilibrium of one's body image (cf. Weiss 1999: 17).[17] Disruption and healing of the body's equilibrium affect human bodies as "at once a biological organism, a ground of personal identity, and a social construct"(Leder 1990: 99). Instances of pain or other discomfort focus

---

[15] With 'disappearance', Leder does not mean "the vanishing of something that was originally present to the gaze", as the term is commonly used, but "that which never shows itself for structural reasons" (Leder 1990: 27). Dis-appear thus means not-appear.

[16] In a European or Northern American cultural context, that is, since "a certain degree of visceral disappearance can be attributed to Western insensitivities" (Leder 1990: 43).

[17] Sigmund Freud has suggested that illness or pain may magnify afflicted areas in the body image. Such changes then feed back into one's experience of the body (Grosz 1994: 76).

attention on one's own body as an object of experience. The recessive body comes to the fore in times of distress: Mr. Theunissen is constantly aware of his intestines because they hurt all the time.

Leder claims that a body or body part affected by pain or dis-ease emerges as something foreign to the person experiencing it (Leder 1990: 76). Moreover, in medical examinations one's body is transformed into "a collection of organs, a mass to be studied and palpated" (Leder 1990: 98) and the patient incorporates the objectifying gaze of the doctor, as we saw in the example of Mr. Theunissen. Katharine Young, whose ethnographic work on biomedical practices has been inspired by phenomenology, has made a similar argument when she described medical examinations as instances of disembodiment: "(f)rom being a locus of self, patients' bodies are transformed into objects of scrutiny, organs in a sack of flesh" (Young 1989: 46).

Real-time medical imaging involves technological, visual mediations of embodied perceptions and experiences of body parts that Leder has described as absent. Leder considers comparable mediations, like blood samples, a blood pressure meter or an X-ray, to be strategies of reflective observation enabling people to find out about their interior (Leder 1990: 44). He claims that "the absences that haunt my bodily depths are not effaced by this reflective maneuvers" (Leder 1990: 44). The visual perception of one's own colon for example – or rather: of the body parts that can be visualized – does not imply the experience of that colon from within: "(t)he mystery of my body is only heightened by the very strangeness or the organ before me, its phenomenological noncoincidence with my body-as lived" (Leder 1990: 44).[18] It is only through another body, an instrument, or the outer appearance of the own body that one gains access to one's interior. In her book on body images phenomenologist Gail Weiss stated about medical "technologies of the visible":

> That these invasive technologies are often uncomfortable, embarrassing, painful, and alienating, is undeniable, but what also must be affirmed is the way in which they open up (…) bodies to experiences and possibilities that would not be available otherwise. (Weiss 1999: 124)

A phenomenological description of the experience of Mr. Theunissen presents him as an embodied subject, a lived body. The presented fragments are about links between feeling

---

[18] The noncoincidence of perceiver and perceived is not typical for perceptions of the interior body: the eye from which one sees does not coincide with its mirror image either. However, self-perceptions of the exterior, surface body are direct, where visceral perception is largely indirect and require mediation of some sort, often via the surface of the body (Leder 1999: 50).

one's body from within and looking at pictures of the body's interior. A body part that is supposed to be absent from consciousness and that recedes from the patient's body image comes to the fore in a state of dysfunction – it dys-appears (Leder 1990: 83) Phenomenology offers a rich vocabulary to overcome the gap between the patient as an ill person and as a diseased body. Yet, phenomenological descriptions of technological mediations of embodiment present images and bodies as distinct categories of representation and experience. My question is *how* real-time visual representations get translated into embodied experiences and vice versa. To address that question, I need a way to describe the work of technology that is more specific about the mediating role of technologies than the phenomenological framework that I have presented here.

Bodily translations: vocabularies from science and technology studies

Mr. Coenen is in his early fifties. Since an ultrasound examination twenty years ago he knows that he suffers from a medical condition that also has affected several of his relatives: polycystic kidney disease. Both his kidneys are full of cysts: follicles filled with liquid.

MC	I have known that I have this condition for twenty years now. It actually started with hypertension. I have been under medical supervision ever since, but well: it is far away, it does not really bother you, you just wait and see. And then, at a certain point in time, you start having problems here and there, hypertension and stuff…
MR	And you had to come for check-ups?
MC	Yes, every year. But now it is somewhat more intensive, now it is once every six weeks that I come here.
MR	You had hypertension, and other symptoms as well?
MC	Yes. My feet are usually somewhat swollen, but actually that was it. Apart from that, things went pretty well for me.

Over the past few years, cysts have grown in number and size and Mr. Coenen's kidney functions have deteriorated.

MR	Does it affect your daily life?
MC	Yes, lately it does, it has recently started. Once a week I go running a bit with a friend of mine. Until two years ago, we ran for ten kilometers, but there is not much left of that. If I can keep it up for one kilometer now, well, that is some achievement. I get

tired sooner in everyday activities as well. Considerable hypertension lately. That is how you come to notice. Fitness goes downhill. That is how you notice.

The attending specialist expects that soon Mr. Coenen's kidneys will stop functioning altogether. Just recently, a series of examinations, including an ultrasound of the abdomen and kidneys, has been initiated in preparation for haemodialysis[19] and ultimately transplantation. When his blood values will reach a certain level and his hypertension is under control by medication, Mr. Coenen will start dialysis. The next step will be transplantation. That may take a long time: the current waiting list for a kidney transplant is four years.

Mr. Coenen's kidney problem was diagnosed by means of ultrasound and monitored through a variety of imaging and other technologies: lab technologies measuring the blood value, a blood pressure meter, medication. These technologies have become part of Mr. Coenen's experience of his body and illness. Parts of the body that most people usually do not consciously experience, have become manifest for Mr. Coenen. He feels that his condition is getting worse and he tries to imagine what goes on inside him, informed by medical data provided by doctors and technological devices.

An anthropological description of Mr. Coenen's situation would most likely be phrased in terms of doctor-patient communication and of the impact of a professional explanatory model on a lay explanatory model. Equally, from an anthropological framework I would focus on expressions of embodiment in Mr. Coenen's story. A narrative analysis could be complemented by an account of Mr. Coenen's subjectivation, i.e. the way he internalizes the biomedical image of his body. From a phenomenological perspective, I would focus more closely on Mr. Coenen's perceptions of his own body as they are grounded in his existence as an embodied subject. Yet, what most anthropologists and phenomenologists would ignore is how technologies actually interfere with bodies: how does ultrasound mediate how doctors as well as patients know what is going on inside their bodies? And how does ultrasound affect patients' experiences?

In order to describe what technologies do, I turn to *actor-network theory* (ANT) as it has been shaped and reconceptualized in the work of Bruno Latour (1987, 1999a &b, 2005), Michel Callon (1986), John Law (1992, 1999) and Madeleine Akrich (1992).[20] Initially

---

[19] In hemodialysis, artificial kidneys remove by-products from the blood when the kidneys are unable to do so.
[20] From the large body of ANT-work I have selected here only some of the works that have inspired me.

developed as a sociology of objects and objectivation, it has incited a body of work that could be called a sociology of subjectivation. To appreciate the latter body of work some understanding of its background is indispensable. Before turning to what has been referred to as the 'second wave' of ANT (Latour 1999b: 23), I therefore present the basic ideas of ANT through a short introduction of the work of Latour.

Latour's material semiotics is rooted in an a-modern ontology and includes a particular conceptualization of how technologies mediate action. Modern distinctions between subject and object, nature and society, mind and body, hamper an understanding of the world, Latour states. Many entities escape classification in terms of those dichotomies: human bodies incorporate technological devices, machines are inscribed with human properties. Such hybrids render any a priori distinction between human and non-human actors obsolete. The eventual identities of humans and things are not given, but result from the relations between entities. To study technological culture means to trace and disentangle the processes that transform entities. Only then does it become clear that many entities are actually hybrids of human and non-human qualities (Latour 1993a).

As an alternative to a representationalist epistemology, Latour has introduced the concept of 'circulating reference' (Latour 1999a: 24-79). The basic idea is that 'reference' does not start from either a (natural) object or a textual, visual or other representation, but can only be understood as the result of a series of transformations and adaptations of both text and object, knowledge and world, image and body. An object of knowledge – e.g. a patient's body – does not precede a particular representation. The ultrasound pictures that appear before Mr. Coenen neither resemble his kidneys, nor do they depict a fixed condition of polycystic kidney disease. Throughout this book I show how medical images and patients' bodies are linked to each other in series of translations that entail material transformations: "phenomena are what *circulates* all along the reversible chain of transformations, at each step losing some properties to gain others" (Latour 1999a: 71, emphasis in original). The phenomenon that is traced in this investigation is disease/illness – as a category of medical knowledge as well as a mode of embodied experience. The particular qualities this phenomenon acquires result from the process of real-time imaging and carry its traces.

The concept of mediation is central to Latour's philosophy of technology. Technological mediation has four meanings: goal translation, composition, reversible blackboxing and delegation (Latour 1999a: 174-215). First, a particular network of human and non-human actors emerges from an attempt by one of those actors to *translate* a particular *goal* into the purpose of others, thus enrolling them into the network. In the above example,

Mr. Coenen can be described as an actor-network consisting of his body, a physician, an imaging device and moving pictures on a monitor. Mr. Coenen's goal to restore his health or manage his illness is translated into a diagnostic purpose that involves imaging technologies. In that process Mr. Coenen himself is transformed into an object and into an instrument of medical imaging that needs to be prepared in order to play those roles.

Second, *agency* is a *composed* property of associated human and non-human agents (Latour 1999a: 182). In the above case, the ultrasound device and the pictures actively shape how the radiologist as well as Mr. Coenen produce and acquire knowledge about the latter's kidneys. The work involved in the construction of an actor-network and the composition of action is often rendered invisible in philosophical and social-scientific accounts of technology. This is the third element of technological mediation: *black-boxing*. When appearing on the monitor, ultrasound pictures do not show how bouncing sound waves have been translated into visual representations. The work entailed in producing a representation, that is, disappears from view. At first sight, the image just refers to Mr. Coenen's kidneys. Yet for a proper understanding of technological mediation, black boxes need to be opened up to show the translations and compositions that underlie particular actions (Latour 1999a: 184-5).

The fourth meaning of mediation identified by Latour is *delegation*. Network formation can be delegated from humans to things. Translation of a goal then entails a material transformation. A speed bump – one of Latour's examples – translates the legislator's goal to protect pedestrians into the car owner's interest to protect his car. The material presence of the concrete bump invites a certain kind of behavior: slow down your driving speed (Latour 1999a: 186 ff.). In the case of real-time imaging, the pictures on the monitor may play a similar role. The physician's goal is to plan medical treatment in order to improve Mr. Coenen's health, yet he delegates the task to localize and identify the object of treatment to the ultrasound device. The pictures invite doctor as well as patient to watch them rather than focus on the body itself. Madeleine Akrich has introduced the term 'script' to describe such processes: "like a film script, technical objects define a framework of action together with the actors and the space in which they are supposed to act" (Akrich 1992: 208).

The vocabulary and analytical framework of Latour has been elaborated in empirical studies of techno-medical practices, such as in Bernike Pasveer's work on X-ray technology (1989, 1992) and in what Latour has called the 'second wave' of science studies (Latour

1999b: 23).[21] Where actor-network theory originated as an alternative to conceptualizations of the objective world , several authors engaged in an analogous analysis of subjectivity, since "(s)ubjectivity, corporeality, is no more a property of humans, of individuals, of intentional subjects, than being an outside reality is a property of nature" (ibid.). The idea that people *have* bodies and *are* bodies has become a cliché in most contemporary philosophy, social sciences and (elite) every-day language (Mol and Law 2004: 1).[22] ANT-inspired studies like Stefan Hirschauer's description of relations between experience and representation in surgical operations (Hirschauer 1991) and Charis Cussins' account of the medical treatment of female patients in an infertility clinic (Cussins 1998), attempt to bypass rather than overcome canonical dualisms such as object/subject, nature/culture, body/mind.[23] In the words of Latour, authors from the 'second wave' of ANT have prolonged the chains of translation, to include lived bodies (Latour 1999a: 70): "(t)he 'lived body' is not reduced by its encounters with things and technologies – rather, these encounters are what brings it to its specific life" (Berg and Akrich 2004: 9). Medical sociological and anthropological concepts of the body, as elaborated by authors such as Bryan Turner (1992), Emily Martin (1987, 1994) and Nancy Scheper-Hughes and Margaret Lock (1998 (1987)), work done in the field of cultural studies (e.g. Cartwright 1995) and feminist work on embodiment (e.g. Butler 1993, Franklin 1997, Grosz 1994, Haraway 1991) have been sources of inspiration for those authors. Through this expansion of actor-network theory, a material- semiotic approach to embodiment can contribute to "acknowledge the body's active status as agent without implying its immediate, pre-fixed presence, in other words considering it as a 'material-semiotic generative node' which is fundamentally both discursive and material, both historical and real" (Berg and Akrich 2004: 3).

Along similar lines, my analysis of technological mediations of illness experience includes the materiality of techno-scientific practices, thus emphasizing the active, mediating role of objects (medical images) in shaping categories (illness) that are often considered as subjective or social (Berg and Akrich 2004: 2). My aim is to describe "that which allows the subject to emerge – never alone, never a pristine individual, but rather always entangled with

---

[21] That so-called 'second wave', exemplified by Law and Hassard 1999, involved some of the 'first wave' authors, such as Michel Callon, John Law and Bruno Latour himself, as well.

[22] When writing about the human body in relation to medicine, Michel Foucault (1975) has suggested that the subject/object distinction was only established in the early 19th century. With the 'birth of the clinic', an epistemic shift occurred, in which diseases were no longer considered as foreign entities that inhabited bodies, but as conditions of bodies (Mol and Law 2003: 2).

[23] A particularly interesting selection of work along those lines has been published in a special issue of the journal Body and Society, entitled *Bodies on Trial: Performances and Politics in Medicine and Biology* (Berg & Akrich 2004).

and generously gifted by a collective, by objects, techniques, constraints" (Gomart and Hennion 1999: 220).

A particularly interesting spin-off of ANT is the work of the Dutch philosopher Annemarie Mol. In *The Body Multiple* (2002) she shows how a particular disease (arteriosclerosis) is enacted in socio-material medical practices.[24] One of the dualisms Mol explicitly attempts to bypass in *The Body Multiple* is that between illness and disease. She presents patients with their perceptions and experiences as co-constituting the object of biomedicine: disease. Whereas the implications of her ontology-in-practice for patients' experiences of embodiment and illness are not explicitly addressed in *The Body Multiple*, Mol has hinted at the possibilities of an empirical turn for opening the black box of subjectivity in ways analogous to ANT opening the boxes of objectivity (cf. Mol and Law 2004). That move fits my primary goal of understanding how illness comes about as a category of experience and to find out how the production of disease as an epistemological category affects that experience.

A material-semiotic analysis of the case of Mr. Coenen affords a description of the active contribution of ultrasound technology and images to the construction of Mr. Coenen's body as an object of medical examination and the subjectivation it implies. What remains un(der)theorized within this approach, however, is how Mr. Coenen's *experience* is mediated by ultrasound technology. I want to know how technologies interfere with patients' experiences of their bodies and illness. A confrontation of phenomenological and material-semiotic frameworks could join the best of both worlds, for phenomenology does theorize experience but forgets about its 'mediatedness', and ANT theorizes mediated subjectivity but still leaves the category of experience to itself, that is to remain a subjective category in the traditional sense of the word. I turn to post-phenomenology as an example of such a confrontation.

---

[24] Mol has introduced the term *enact* as a 'neutral' alternative for *make, do, construct* or *perform*, which have various distracting connotations (cf. Mol 2002: 32*). Enactment* "suggests that activities take place – but leaves the actors vague. It also suggests that in the act, and only then and there, something *is* – being enacted" (Mol 2002: 33).

"Bodies in technology": post-phenomenological vocabularies

Forty-five- year-old Mrs. Timmer is in a wheelchair. Severe arteriosclerosis[25] - a condition that some of her relatives suffer from as well - has caused chronic heart and lung problems, amputation of a leg, shriveling of a kidney, and a variety of other problems. She can only manage a minimum of physical exercise. She has had over 30 operations. Over the years several organs have been removed: the gallbladder, the appendix and parts of the pancreas. She has had over eighty radiological examinations - among which many arteriographies[26] - over the past five years and many other tests as well. Six months ago she was released from a one-year stay in the hospital. She underwent a major heart operation and additional surgery. She has been readmitted twice over the past six months. She is home now and regularly sees doctors in the hospital for check-ups who then often refer her for yet another examination. Sometimes she does not even know what is checked. This time she has been referred for an ultrasound examination by an internist at the request of her regular lung specialist. Only upon asking the radiologist, she finds out that this time they are looking at the liver. She does not know why, but tells me after the examination that it might have to do with having been an alcoholic.

Mrs. Timmer checks her own blood pressure regularly with a sphygmomanometer provided by the hospital. Because of arteriosclerosis the blood does not flow smoothly to her heart, which is then unable to pump the blood around properly, causing hypertension, Mrs. Timmer explains to me. When the blood pressure values are too high she has to call the doctor. However, since she has become used to the high figures, she only calls when high blood pressure coincides with chest pain or an extremely quick pulse: Mrs. Timmer has her own pulse meter as well. In case of hypertension with pain or a high pulse, Mrs. Timmer or her husband calls the doctor. Usually an ambulance is then sent to take her to the hospital, where she is administered nitro-glycerin by pump to dilate the arteries.

The body of Mrs. Timmer has been transformed by various medical technologies many times and in many ways. Although Mrs. Timmers does not understand all the implications of high-tech interventions, devices like the blood-pressure meter and the pulse meter have become part of her every-day routine. Through these meters Mrs. Timmer has learned how to perceive

---

[25] Stenosis of the arteries.
[26] Fluoroscopic (X-ray) examination of the arteries with use of contrast fluid.

her body in different ways. Absent parts of her body get articulated in numbers and pictures. To assess her body's condition Mrs. Timmer combines such technological representations of bodily functions with how she perceives it from inside. Medical objectivations of her body have also transformed what is her capacity to perceive, know and act (cf. Willems 2005).

The case of Mrs. Timmer shows why the three conceptual frameworks presented in this chapter are not sufficient for my purpose: an analysis of how real-time medical imaging technologies affect patients' *experiences* of health and illness. The anthropological distinction of illness and disease and the subject/object dualism it implies, hampers an integrated account of intertwined processes of objectivation and subjectivation of patients' bodies. Moreover, interpretative medical anthropology and constructivist medical sociology do not do justice to the complex workings of technology and the material aspects of embodiment. The strength of a phenomenological account would be that it affords a relational understanding of subjectivity and objectivity. A person's body is ultimately an embodied subject. From a phenomenological perspective, however, medical objectivations move bodies away from selves (e.g. Leder 1990: 44). Finally, an actor-network approach allows a description of the active role of technologies in the construction of bodies as objects and subjects of knowledge and experience. However, ANT lacks the vocabulary to describe how perceptions are translated into experiences that, despite having emerged from particular constellations of people and things, feel 'purely' individual. None of the frames offers an encompassing vocabulary to describe "bodies in technology" [27]: how technological images interfere with embodied experience.

The technological mediation of human experience is a central theme in the work of American philosopher of technology Don Ihde. Ihde has complemented a phenomenological interest in human perception with a fascination for technology. The expansion of phenomenology emerging from this confrontation has become known as *post-phenomenology*.[28] Ihde and other post-phenomenologists, such as the Dutch philosopher of technology Peter-Paul Verbeek, understand phenomenology in terms of the actual descriptions and analyses written by scholars like Husserl and Merleau-Ponty. Phenomenology has inadvertently been presented by its protagonists as a method for the description of reality by turning to the things themselves (Verbeek 2005: 107). That image has

---

[27] Cf. Ihde 2002.

[28] The term 'postphenomenology' has been used to refer to various authors and schools of thinking expanding phenomenology in one way or another, or to refer to the work of authors such as Derrida, Levinas and Irigaray. In my argument, however, post-phenomenology denotes the expansion of phenomenology into the philosophy of technology.

provoked criticism of phenomenology's subjectivism and introspection (e.g. Latour in Ihde 2003: 9).

What the early phenomenologists actually did, however, is different from what they claimed to do. The work of Merleau-Ponty especially offers building blocks for a phenomenology that is not susceptible to the above-mentioned criticism. In his *Phénoménologie de la perception* (1962), Merleau-Ponty has not provided a description of reality, but has analyzed the relations between human beings and the world. His primary object of analysis have been the perceptual interrelations between humans and the world. Neither a perceiving subject nor a perceived object are his point of departure, but the relations between them. He has described perception as a relation in which an interior subject and an exterior object are constituted (Verbeek 2005: 108 ff.). Post-phenomenological analyses of technology present experience as a *relational* category, building on actual phenomenological work rather than unsubstantiated claims by phenomenologists and their critics.

According to post-phenomenological theory, technologies of all kinds mediate people's perceptions and interpretations of the world and the ways in which reality is present for people. Analyzing technological mediations of scientific perceptions of the world, Don Ihde has identified two dimensions of perception: microperception and macroperception. Microperceptions are the sensory perceptions, often mediated by instruments, that (scientific) knowledge is built on. A patient's or a doctor's visual perceptions of medical images, or the interior sensations of a patient, are microperceptions. Macroperceptions are the cultural frames of reference against which reality is understood: the medico-cultural knowledge about a link between liver problems and alcoholism for example, that led Mrs. Timmer to think that her health problems might be related to her heavy drinking. Microperceptions and macroperceptions can be analytically distinguished but can never be separated in practice (Ihde 1990: 29).

Technological instruments can mediate micro- as well as macroperceptions. That goes for every-day perceptions as much as for scientific observations. People often relate to the world via a technical device. Some devices, such as glasses, almost become part of one's body. They are transparent, i.e. they pass aspects of the world without being explicitly present as such an aspect themselves. Ihde calls such relations between a person and a technological device, *embodiment* relations (Ihde 1990: 72 ff.). Other devices, such as a thermometer, invite a *hermeneutical relation*: they offer a representation of an aspect of the world, which cannot merely be perceived, but requires interpretation (Ihde 1990: 80 ff.). Human-technology relations may also be of a different kind than mediation. People may also relate to a *technology itself*, rather than to the world through a technological device (Ihde 1990: 97 ff.). A technology may also form the *background* for a perception, without being the object of perception itself (Ihde 1990: 108 ff.).

Verbeek has drawn upon the work of Ihde in his search for a vocabulary to describe the roles that technological artifacts play in people's perceptions of the world. He emphasizes that technologies do not mediate between subjects and objects, or people and the world, but shape the perceptual and experiential relations from which subjects and objects emerge. Technological mediations can be situated along a continuum of embodied and hermeneutical relations. Mrs. Timmer's body is affected by medical technology in two interrelated ways: technological devices mediate how she perceives her body and at the same time fashion the body that appears to her. The numbers on the blood pressure meter *represent* her body's condition only because she has learned how to interpret them. Medical images, on the other hand, seem to *present* a direct view inside. In fact, the distinction between hermeneutical and embodiment relations is not always strict. When Mrs. Timmer watches the monitor during an ultrasound examination she sees parts of her body. Much of what she sees, however, she would not recognize without the radiologist's explanations.

In *Bodies in Technology* (2002) Don Ihde reflects upon technological mediations of embodiment. The post-phenomenological body is an agent of perception, interpretation and existence in and of the world. Ihde proposes to substitute 'embodiment' for 'subjectivity', thus taking into account the situatedness and materiality of human experience (Ihde 2002: 11). What such a substitution obscures, however, is that people's bodies are also part of 'the world' or 'reality' and therefore objects of perception and interpretation. In experiences of real-time medical imaging, patients are subjects as well as objects of visualization.

Ihde has distinguished two modes of embodiment: the here-body (or body one) and the image-body (or body two). The first is the embodied subject that moves, perceives, senses and is-in-the-world (Ihde 2002: xi). The *here-body* is the patient who talks to me,[29] feels pain and watches a monitor. The body patients talk about, feel and look at is what Ihde has called an *image-body*: one's own body as an object of perception. The image-body is the object of macro-perception: it is the culturally informed and shaped signification of a particular sensory microperception (Ihde 2002: 5). The image-body does not coincide with the here-body, but they cannot meaningfully be separated either. Mrs. Timmer's relation to her own body is mediated by various technologies. Her own body is the here-body feeling a fast heartbeat and

---

[29] The researcher, MR.

reading the blood pressure meter, as well as the body-at-risk, identified as such according to exterior, objective medical standards.

My question about technological mediations of bodies as subjects and as objects of (illness) experience, addresses the co-construction of patients' here-bodies and image-bodies in practices of real-time medical imaging. I share with Ihde the specific interest in how people experience themselves through or with artifacts (Ihde 2002: xiii). Embodiment is an intertwined process of objectivation and subjectivation that can be mediated by technologies. An analysis of either here-bodies or image-bodies misses a crucial quality of embodied experience: that it is neither objective nor subjective, but enacted in relations between bodies and images. To describe such relations, Ihde links bodily materiality to technology, for "technologies are the material aspects of our embodied ways of relating to the world" (Ihde 2002: 20). The strength of post-phenomenology for my analysis lies in its explicit inclusion of materiality in perception and experience, in particular of the role of instruments in making the world present for people.

Besides mediating people's interpretations of reality, technologies interfere with people's existence in the world. Verbeek has extended Ihde's work on technological mediations of perceptions to include praxis, or the existential dimensions of technological mediation. Therefore, he has challenged "Latour's declaration that phenomenology is incompatible with his position" (Verbeek 2005: 162) and has read Latour's work on technical mediation through post-phenomenological glasses. Verbeek argues that unlike classical phenomenology, a post-phenomenological perspective

> comes much closer to Latour's perspective on the relations between human and non-humans. It deals with subjects and objects, not as pregiven entities that assume relations with each other, but as entities that are constituted in their mutual relation. Human beings are what they are by virtue of the way in which they realize their existence in their world, and their world is what it is by virtue of the way in which it can manifest itself in the relations humans have to it. Thus postphenomenology does not draw a line between two poles, but rather lets the poles emerge from the line that constitutes them. (Verbeek 2005: 163)

A major difference between Latour's actor-network theory and post-phenomenology is that the latter analytically distinguishes (human) subjects from (human or nonhuman) objects, although it is acknowledged that they can hardly be separated in practice (Verbeek 2005: 164). Whereas Latour is primarily interested in how hybrid actants come into being in networks of relations, post-phenomenology aims at an in-depth understanding of the relations people have with such emerging entities (Verbeek 2005: 164-5). I argue that an analysis of techno-visual mediations of embodied experience needs both: an extended description of the networks from which bodies emerge as well as a detailed account of how people experience those bodies.

Mrs. Timmer has not only learned how to perceive and interpret her body through various technical devices, she has also shaped her existence in relation to a blood pressure meter, a pulse meter and an emergency phone number. For Mrs. Timmer, real-time images are among many other technological presentations of her interior body. It is this particular category of techno-visual mediation that I am interested in. A description of technologically mediated embodiment 'from the middle' – starting with technological practices – results in a body that cannot self-evidently be distinguished as an object or a subject. In my analyses, I will show how processes of objectivation and subjectivation of patient bodies are intertwined.

Conceptual confrontations

Patients' trajectories of real-time imaging start at the onset or suspicion of illness. Many people visit a doctor when their body feels or looks different than normal or when there is other reason to suspect that something might be wrong. The doctor can refer a patient for further examination, for instance by means of ultrasound, fluoroscopy or endoscopy – the real-time imaging technologies around which I build my analysis, and which may be used for diagnostic as well as for screening purposes. Medical anthropology and the sociology of health and illness offer a rich vocabulary for the study of illness as a cultural phenomenon and a subjective and intersubjective experience which is primarily expressed and disclosed in narratives. Their vocabulary to describe the work of (medical) technologies, however, is relatively poor. In the anthropological distinction between disease and illness, technology is associated with disease, i.e. the medical professional outlook on (ill-)health. Moreover, technology plays a one-dimensional role as an intermediary between a physical body and a professional observer. Technology is therefore said to widen the gap between disease and illness (Helman 2001: 166). Instead of assuming such a gap, I intend to explore how the situatedness of biomedical knowledge may constitute and shape particular embodied experiences and identities, or the "circumstances under which different modes of experience arise" (Jackson 1996: 25).

Whereas in anthropology and sociology illness as a category of experience is usually distinguished from disease as an object of knowledge, a review of current insights from post-phenomenology and the sociology of translation suggests that a focus on material practices and technological mediation blurs that distinction. What fascinates me is how using and producing a particular kind of knowledge - medical knowledge in real-time medical imaging practices - is intertwined with using and producing particular kinds of embodied experience – illness experiences of patients who go through real-time imaging.

Anthropological conceptualizations of embodiment have focused more on ideas than on practices. To address anthropological questions about illness experience, however, the turn to practices is just as essential as it has been for understanding the construction of medical knowledge (cf. Mol 2002). Studying experience through its (narrative) expressions, as anthropologists have done, affords descriptions of illness as a socio-cultural phenomenon. What is largely missing from anthropological accounts of illness experience is the body's materiality. A narrative bias, a poor vocabulary for material aspects of experience, an instrumental definition of technology, and the illness/disease dualism are the main shortcomings of an interpretative social-scientific framework. My analysis aims at an integrated understanding of illness as a material-discursive phenomenon. With its detailed accounts of expressions of illness experience grounded in profound ethnographic fieldwork, however, medical anthropology offers an indispensable background for my argument.

Phenomenology offers an alternative for narrative analyses of experience. It situates all human experience, including illness, inside the body and it offers an elaborate conceptual framework to describe embodied experience. My question is how the material translation of the interior body in images may affect patients' body images at the level of individual microperceptions as well as at the level of socio-cultural macroperceptions and how imaging may establish links between those levels. A phenomenological framework is also appealing because it presents experience not merely as a relation between objects and subjects, but as a constitutive force combining both. Phenomenological analyses of illness and other bodily perceptions, however, are somewhat unsatisfactory. With regard to my research question, what is problematic about phenomenology is that it presupposes that technology is an intermediary that alienates bodies from selves.

The main strength of actor-network theory is the presentation of technology as a mediator rather than an intermediary. For me as a medical anthropologist, the inclusion of material actors offers a refreshing perspective on well-known problems that usually have been framed in discursive terms, and a way out of unproductive dualisms such as disease and illness. However, an analysis in terms of emerging agencies leaves little room for perception and experience as embodied qualities of human beings:

> The facts that technological artifacts can be conceived as constructions, always exist in a context, and are interpreted by human beings in terms of their specific frameworks of reference do not erase the fact that systematic reflection can be undertaken of the role that these contextual and interpreted constructions play concretely in the experience and behavior of human beings. That "the things themselves" are accessible only in mediated ways does not interfere with our ability to say something about the roles that they play, thanks to their mediated identities, in their environment. And it is precisely the postphenomenological perspective that offers a new way of so doing. (Verbeek 2005: 113)

Post-phenomenology has resulted from attempts to merge the best of both worlds, being phenomenology and actor-network theory. It presents technology as constitutive of embodied subjectivity as well as of the objectifications of bodies, yet maintains the distinction between human subjects and objects that may be human as well as non-human. Experience is relational, situated, material and embodied yet ultimately belongs to the human realm. In a (post-)phenomenological framework, "what the world 'is', and what subjects 'are', arises from the interplay between humans and reality" (Verbeek 2003: 93). Yet it assumes that objectivity is an attribute of the world, whereas subjectivity is ascribed to "those who are experiencing and existing in it" (ibid.).

> A philosophy that is to have any hope of grasping the every-day reality of human beings needs to acknowledge this difference and to show that making a distinction between them can never imply an actual separation. (Verbeek 2005: 167)

A major drawback of the post-phenomenological focus on experiential relations is that it risks to loose sight of the conditions under which such relations emerge – the kind that ANT can describe so well. I will argue that real-time imaging offers a context in which the emergence of here-bodies and image-bodies is inextricably intertwined.

The matrix on the next page provides a schematic summary of the building blocks collected in this chapter in order to develop a more comprehensive analytical frame throughout this book. Missing from the matrix are the specific characteristics of the empirical field; the technology in question is a *visualization* technology that produces moving pictures of parts of patients' *interior* bodies which can be *watched* in *real-time* by both doctors and *patients*. In the following chapters I use empirical material to introduce these specific features of the particular kind of technologically mediated embodied experiences that I am interested in. It will result in a more sophisticated, layered understanding of illness.

	Medical anthropology / sociology of health and illness	Phenomenology	Actor-network theory	Post-phenomenology
Embodiment	body is object of individual perception, social relations and political structures; 'mindful body'	- body is basis of all subjective experience; 'lived body' - body image is constitutive of embodied identity	bodies are articulated in networks of humans and non-humans	body is both embodied subject and (disembodied) object of perception ;'here-body / image-body'
Experience	experience is (inter-) subjective and mainly represented by and disclosed in narratives	- experience denotes relation between subject and object - all experience is embodied - part of body is absent from experience	- analysis in terms of agency rather than experience - no essential difference between humans and non-humans - subjectivity and objectivity are circulating capacities	- technological devices mediate embodied subject and perceived body - human experience is situated and material
Illness	contrast between disease (object of professional knowledge) and illness (object of lay experience)	- illness alienates body from self	- disease emerges from hybrid configurations of actors, including patients' bodies	not explicitly addressed
Technological mediation	- technology widens gap between disease and illness - technology is intermediary between subject and object	technological representations of body's functions transform object of perception yet do not alter embodied experience	- technology is congealed labor - technology mediates action and transforms entities involved in action	technology mediates embodied perception as well as embodied existence/action
Main strength with regard to research question	rich vocabulary for study of illness as a cultural phenomenon	- rich vocabulary for study of embodied experience - body image as mediator between body and self	- rich vocabulary for study of material agency and emergence of hybrid actors - non-dualist framework	rich vocabulary for study of technological mediation of embodiment
Main weakness with regard to research question	- narrative bias - illness/disease dualism - instrumental view of technology	- technology is passive intermediary - technology implies alienation	poor vocabulary to describe technological mediation of perception and experience	focus on experiential relation between subject and object too narrow

After the explorations of conceptual and theoretical grounds in this chapter, I can now formulate a research question that does not presuppose a distinction between bodies as objects and as subjects and which explicitly reflects my interest in this issue as a medical anthropologist:

> *How do real-time medical imaging technologies that enable doctors as well as patients to watch live moving pictures of part of the interior body, mediate patients' embodied experiences of illness and health?*

I have introduced the core concepts for this question: *embodiment, experience, illness and technological mediation*. In the following chapters I will sow those conceptual 'seeds' into the 'soil' of real-time imaging practices.

Real-time imaging provides a point of entrance to address relations between technologies and people's existence and perceptions as embodied beings, especially in times of illness. Although my research question about techno-visual mediations of embodied experience resonates with post-phenomenology, it is impossible for me to decide which subject-object relation to focus on without a thorough exploration of the field of real-time imaging in a broad sense. In my argument I will present an actor-network analysis of the enactment of patient bodies as composite objects, instruments and subjects of medical imaging (in chapters 3 and 4) before initiating an analysis of embodied experience (in chapter 5). I develop a framework to address the hermeneutic and existential significations of real-time image perception and to evaluate which are the patient bodies that are presented to and present for the various actors involved.

Mol has convincingly shown how the empirical turn in philosophy – starting from practices rather than from ideas – affords a shift from epistemological questions about doctors' ability to know bodies to the ontological question of which bodies are enacted in particular practices (Mol 2002). It opens up the black box of 'objectivity' and renders problematic dualisms between subject and object obsolete. In the same vein, I look for alternative ways to address anthropological and phenomenological concerns about illness as a mode of technologically mediated embodied experience, thus opening up the black box of 'subjectivity'. Mol includes patients' experiences in her reconceptualization of *disease*. I include a description of medical knowledge production involving bodies, machines, flesh and blood in a reconceptualization of *illness*. The experienced body is 'contaminated' by the body as an object of medical knowledge (Akrich and Pasveer 2004: 81). If the notion of an embodied person is taken seriously, the physical and lived body often appear to be practiced as one. However, they can be separated in the same practices. Embodiment, health and illness may come in different modalities that result from rather than explain particular practices. How that actually happens in practices of real-time medical imaging is the topic of the following chapters.

3 Patient compositions: preparing bodies for real-time imaging

Not just any body can be visualized. Bodies need to be prepared in order to be translated into medical images. In this chapter I discuss how bodies are transformed in preparations for real-time imaging by various human and non-human actors involved: visualization devices, professional image-makers, patients and papers. The aggregate analysis of the emergence of a generic patient body 'ready for real-time imaging' is based on field observations of individual patients and of particular ultrasound, fluoroscopy and endoscopy examinations. I use an actor-network approach to describe what happens to bodies before they end up on an examination table and on a monitor. Thus I show how preparations set up the conditions under which real-time medical images can eventually transform embodied experience.

To produce meaningful data, real-time imaging requires the simultaneous presence of an appropriate and working imaging device, a competent doctor, a collaborative patient, a prepared body and a well-articulated request. The first four sections of the chapter subsequently discuss the configuration of imaging devices, medical professionals, patients and request forms for their eventual positions in networks of real-time imaging. The individual and joint preparations of the human and non-human actors in those networks constitute a process of *collective embodiment*: a body 'ready-for-imaging' that is both singular and multiple (cf. Mol 2002: 84). In preparations for real-time imaging, bodies and their potential medical conditions are articulated in various modes: as passive objects of examination, as active co-producers of knowledge, as material entities of a particular kind, as a person, or as some other kind of entity – or a combination of many of these. Collective embodiment entails both objectivations and subjectivations of patients' bodies: the configuration of patients' bodies as objects of medical examination and sensory perception affects how their agency as eventual spectators and collaborators in a real-time imaging event is shaped. Patients' active contribution to their body's preparation, in turn, transforms the body that will appear on the monitor in an examination room.

Bodies in machines

The cases for my analysis of technological mediation of embodiment and illness experience are three medical imaging technologies: ultrasound, fluoroscopy and endoscopy. The three technologies differ in their technical specifications, in their clinical applications and in their professional contexts of use. Ultrasound and fluoroscopy are radiological technologies, whereas endoscopy belongs to the realm of surgery. Ultrasound, fluoroscopy and endoscopy can all be used to visualize various parts of the interior body. Endoscopes are used to enter bodily cavities such as the stomach, the uterus or the prostate, but also lungs or knee joints, both with a camera and with small surgical instruments. Ultrasound is best known for its obstetric and gynecological uses, in particular during pregnancy. My analysis, however, is limited to radiological and endoscopic visualizations of parts of the intestinal and of the urinary tract made primarily for diagnostic reasons, i.e. in order to locate physical abnormalities that cause illness or increase the risk for illness. Moreover, I have selected only those examinations that enable patients to watch the moving images produced by means of those devices in real-time. The apparently direct visual access to one's own interior body has triggered my fascination for the relation between technological representations and embodied experiences of human bodies. In the present section, I provide a concise introduction to the technical set-up of each of those types of machines, as they are used in the radiology and endoscopy departments where I carried out my fieldwork.

Moving x-ray pictures: fluoroscopic spectacles and spectators

X-rays, discovered in 1895 by the German physicist Wilhelm Röntgen, are invisible electro-magnetic waves that are sent through a human body. Since Röntgen's discovery, X-ray images have become cultural icons for clinical diagnostics of the living body's interior. X-rays are able to penetrate soft tissue, but are absorbed by bones. A sheet of sensitive film placed behind the body is struck by different quantities of X-rays, resulting in an image that shows interior body structures on the basis of the variety in tissue composition and mass. Body parts can be distinguished because they react differently to X-rays. Bones, containing calcium, do not allow much radiation to pass, and result in white shapes on an X-ray film. The air-filled lungs allow nearly all X-rays to pass, resulting in a black film image. When body parts are not distinctive enough, external substances must be added to the body to produce contrast. Different degrees of permeability in bodily tissue and contrast substances render normal and abnormal structures inside the body visually discernable.

The use of contrast substances is particular common in fluoroscopic examinations, which use X-rays to produce moving images of a particular organ in action. Fluoroscopic images on a monitor are negatives of normal X-ray pictures: bones appear as black, air as white. Moving, fluoroscopic images depict more than the structures common X-ray pictures present. Fluoroscopic pictures show how particular organs or objects inside the body move, or are obstructed. The clinical implications of such pictures are not self-evident. Radiologists receive specialized training to interpret and compare fluoroscopic pictures to visual and numerical information obtained by other means.[30]

During a regular X-ray event a relatively high dose of radiation is emitted once or during a few subsequent instances. During a fluoroscopy the X-ray tube is left on, emitting radiation of lower intensity, yet constantly, over a longer period of time. In today's fluoroscopy equipment, like the Philips Diagnost 97-DSI that was used in the examinations I observed, X-rays strike an image intensifier tube rather than a film. The image intensifier produces brighter images than would be possible using a fluorescent screen, as was common in the early days of fluoroscopy. The intensifier tube is connected through a video camera, making images appear on a monitor. If connected to a computer, the fluoroscopic output can be digitally processed and enhanced. The machine can be set to show only the required parameters for a particular purpose, and suppress irrelevant information.

The fluoroscopic examinations of the upper and lower gastro-intestinal and the urinary tract that I observed require patients to take contrast agents, since soft tissues are not clearly visualized with (low-intensity) X-rays. Substances or liquids like barium or iodine absorb X-rays more effectively than the surrounding tissue. For an examination of the upper gastro-intestinal tract, patients need to swallow a barium compound, whereas for inspection of the lower part of the digestive system a contrast agent is administered rectally. To examine bladder and kidney functions, a liquid contrast is administered through a catheter.

The configuration of the fluoroscopic examinations included in my sample allowed patients to watch real-time moving pictures of their own interior body on a monitor, at least during part of the examination. During such examinations, patients are active as spectators. They also contribute to the material transformations of their bodies. For example, during an

---

[30] The training of imaging professionals is discussed later in this chapter.

examination to check for possible reflux of urine to the kidneys the radiologist needs the patient to indicate when his or her bladder is full, and then to empty the bladder on command. And during fluoroscopic examination of the gastro-intestinal tract patients swallow contrast fluid and in addition turn their bodies around on the examination table and alternately adjust to the flexible table's horizontal and vertical positions, operated by the radiologist.

X-rays render the exterior body transparent and the interior body visible for physicians as well as for patients. Many patients are familiar with the kind of (X-ray) pictures that fluoroscopy produces, even if they do not exactly recognize the structures they see or are unaware that the black contours which outline their intestines are caused by contrast substance. While physicians are watching the monitor, they compare what they see to other information on the patient's condition and on the normal fluoroscopic appearance of particular parts of the body. The fluoroscopic representation of an interior body provides them with a visual data-set. In sum, fluoroscopy implies patients' bodies as dynamic visual objects, data-sets and pictures, as well as actors and spectators.

Seeing with sound[31]

Ultrasound is another real-time radiological technology that provides both physicians and patients with visual access to the latter's interior bodies. Like fluoroscopy, it is particularly apt to visualize *dynamic* moving structures inside living bodies. In ultrasound examinations, however, it is not radiation but pulses of very high-frequency sound that pass through the skin into the body. Because different soft tissues and fluids reflect the waves at different speeds, images represent the boundaries between tissues. Since ultrasound is reflected by air or gas, this technology is not very useful to image the bowels. Neither is it possible to visualize what is inside or behind a bony structure. Soft tissues, however, which are hard to visualize by conventional X-ray, can be visualized by means of ultrasound.

The equipment used in the radiology department where I observed examinations was an ATL HDI 5000 ultrasound machine. It produced 2D grey-scale images, sometimes complemented by blue and red indicators of blood flows. Through a microphone-like transducer probe, pressed firmly against the patient's body, high-frequency sound pulses are transmitted into the body and hit boundaries between tissues. Gel is applied to the probe for

---

[31] Title borrowed from (Yoxen 1987).

good acoustic contact between body and transducer, eliminating any air between them. The transducer functions as a loudspeaker that transmits sound waves, as well as a microphone recording the sounds echoed back. The probe is linked to the central processing unit (CPU) of the ultrasound machine and picks up waves which are reflected when they have reached a boundary between tissues of different density and passes them on to the machine. The CPU calculates distances from probe to boundary, using the speed of sound in tissue and the time of the each echo's return. The machine displays the distances and intensities of the echoes on the monitor, forming two-dimensional images of a part of a patient's interior body. Bones and muscles reflecting sound waves show up as white, whereas softer areas and fluids appear dark. The ATL HDI 5000 uses real-time compound imaging, enabling transducers to transmit and receive signals in many different directions, thus increasing the amount of diagnostic information acquired and processed. It is equipped with various programs, with pre-settings for the examination of a particular organs or area. The machine can also visualize the speed of blood flow, e.g. through the kidneys, by calculating the Doppler effect, which is the difference between the high frequency of the transmitted waves and the frequency of the returning sound waves, which is lower as the reflecting surface is more distant.

Whereas a fluoroscopic device directly produces visual data, an ultrasound machine mechanically translates sound waves into numerical data and numbers into pictures. Although both devices produce images, ultrasound does not first of all present the interior body as a visual object, but as a collection of structures and substances with different material characteristics. Where fluoroscopy primarily visualizes structures and movements, ultrasound rather aims at the identification of normal and abnormal locations and distributions of tissue and fluid. The objects of fluoroscopic and ultrasound are therefore distinctively different.

Patients' experiences of ultrasound and fluoroscopic examinations, however, do not seem that different. Most set-ups for ultrasound examinations allow patients to watch the monitor on which the ultrasonographer watches the moving images resulting from her operations of the transducer probe. Many patients are at least as familiar with obstetric ultrasound pictures as they are with X-rays, either from own experience or from the media. The first picture in a new-born baby's photo album today is often an ultrasound scan. However, when the object of imaging is not a baby, but a kidney or another organ, it is not obviously recognized as part of one's own body. The grey-scale images that appear during an ultrasound examination are not easily recognizable as body parts. Although experienced patients may learn to read ultrasound pictures, to most patients ultrasound presents an unfamiliar sight of their body.

Ultrasound examinations require limited activity from patients. Usually no drastic dietary preparations are required. The ultrasound device mostly stays outside the interior body it is supposed to visualize. Small ultrasound probes can be entered through various bodily orifices and ultrasound can be used to monitor an invasive procedure such as a puncture, yet most examinations I observed involved abdominal ultrasound, whereby the transducer was moved across a patient's abdomen or pelvic area. Compared to a fluoroscopic examination, an ultrasound machine requires less physical activity from a patient in order to produce images that are usable for physicians. In different respects, ultrasound stays 'outside' the patient's body. Ultrasound implies 'patient bodies' that can be active spectators on the one hand, but seem to be rather passive objects on the other.

Interior inspections: endoscopic views inside the body

Endoscopy is different from the previously described imaging technologies. An endoscope does not render parts of the body transparent or translate hidden interior parts into visible structures, but literally enters a patient's body. Classifying endoscopy as an imaging technology is not self-evident, since it is a surgical rather than a radiological technique. Endoscopies are performed by surgeons and specialized physicians, such as gastroenterologists, urologists, gynaecologists, or orthopaedists. Other than a radiological body, an endoscopic body is produced by physicians for whom imaging is only one among many tools for data collection.

An endoscope can enter the body through one of its natural orifices or through an artificial opening. In the latter case it is called laparoscopy. In the endoscopy department where my fieldwork was situated, surgeons and gastroenterologists performed endoscopic inspections of various parts of the digestive tract, including the stomach, intestines and bile ducts. During an examination, the monitor shows real-time images transmitted by the lens of a video cable inside the tube of the endoscope. The tube is attached to a control head through which the physician operates the scope. At the other end the control panel is connected to a video processor and a light source. Video-endoscopes are flexible tubes that contain channels for the transmission of light, air and water, a lens, and a passage for small surgical instruments. Endoscopes differ in length, width and available options. A scope used for sigmoidoscopy – the inspection of the first sixty centimeters of the colon – is shorter than a scope used for a colonoscopy, covering the entire large intestine. For my observations, I only selected examinations of the large intestine by means of an endoscope inserted in a patient's rectum, since only during those examinations the patient's and the monitor's positions allowed patients to watch the monitor showing real-time images.

Endoscopy is used for diagnostic as well as therapeutic purposes, such as the selection of locations for tissue sampling or other interventions, which then produce the actual results of the examination. Endoscopes are for instance used for the removal of gallstones by means of a small mechanical device entered through the tube. Endoscopy's main strength today is believed to be its therapeutic potential, since its diagnostic uses are expected to be taken over by virtual endoscopy, in which CT or MRI images are translated by computers into 3D endoscopic views (Lauridsen 1998: 95).[32] Another recent development in the diagnostic realm has been the introduction of the M2A (mouth to anus) camera pill,[33] which is swallowed by a patient and records images of the small intestine which could not be made using conventional endoscopy.

A patient's body as it is anticipated in endoscopic equipment has some features that differ from those of fluoroscopic and ultrasound bodies. Endoscopic images are video pictures of an imaging device moving through a living body. The endoscope transforms the dark tunnels of the interior body into spaces available for visual inspection. Once inside, however, the body is not merely a visual object, but can also be touched, albeit only through technological instruments. The body is available as a source for the acquisition of tissue and as the site of surgical intervention. Unlike fluoroscopy and ultrasound, endoscopy does not render the exterior body transparent, but actually enters the patient's body. Therefore it meets the interior body's material resistance in the form of curvy and crampy intestines. Endoscopy is invasive and demanding for patients and may cause considerable discomfort preparing for, during and after an examination.[34] Besides involving patients as spectators, endoscopic devices also evoke their active participation in subjecting their bodies to the machine's requirements.

---

[32] In the Netherlands clinical applications of virtual endoscopy have been limited so far. Therefore I leave those developments aside for now, although they may have interesting implications for how medical images affect patients' bodies.

[33] By Given Imaging Ltd. in 2001.

[34] Physicians call any intervention that does not involve access to a patient's body through an artificial opening, non-invasive or minimally invasive. I use 'invasive' in another sense here, indicating the intrusion upon patients' physical and mental state of being (cf. Lammer 2002).

Machine-body interactions

Imaging devices are actively involved in the configuration of the bodies that are being examined, visualized, perceived and experienced in real-time imaging events. Before any physical connection has actually been established between them, instruments of real-time imaging already affect the bodies they will be applied to. Imaging devices anticipate opaque and closed bodies, to be rendered transparent and accessible. Conversely, the anticipated bodies shape the design, set-up and intended uses of real-time imaging devices. Intestines, for example, are narrow and curved and can only be entered by flexible endoscopes that dilate the bowels with air.

Each technology brings along its own particular views of the body. Endoscopic and radiological real-time devices approach a body as a container of materially distinct parts or organs. Imaging concerns the translation of material differences into visual distinctions. Machine and body can be adjusted when such differences are not visually obvious. However, imaging devices do not exclusively produce *visual* data. Neither the machines nor their operator *reduce* material differences to visual distinctions. Making pictures is one amongst other means to identify or exclude the presence of abnormalities in an interior body's structures and functions.

Imaging devices inscribe the bodies to be translated into real-time images with particular qualities. Visualization techniques anticipate opaque bodies and interiors that are invisible from the outside, which must be rendered transparent and visible. Bodies are potential objects of visualization as well as objects of other sensory perceptions. To name but a few examples: it is because of a colon's material resistance and the pain it can cause for patients, that endoscopes are made of flexible material; patients' dislike of the sensation of cold gel, used to connect their body to an ultrasound transducer, is the reason behind the installation of gel-warmers in some ultrasound rooms; and a machine used for fluoroscopic examinations of the colon contains a kind of ball that the radiologist can use to pressurize intestinal curves for better pictures.

The configuration of real-time imaging devices thus also takes account of the involvement of bodies as part of the imaging apparatus. The machines are designed to minimize physical resistances and their success is in part dependent on the right balance between the body's passive compliance and active collaboration. For a real-time imaging machine to work, i.e. to produce images that physicians can use, bodies need to be passive objects as well as active cooperators. Required actions vary from activities resembling gymnastic exercises during a colon fluoroscopy to compliance with breathing instructions during an ultrasound examination. Relations between bodies and imaging devices are already being established in the design, set-up and intended use of such devices. The configuration of the machine is closely connected to how patients' interior bodies are prepared to interact with the machine and become visible entities (cf. Prentice 2005).

Typical for the particular applications of real-time imaging that I have studied, when compared to many other medical imaging and other diagnostic practices, is that they allow – or actually invite – patients to be engaged in the examination as spectators. The material qualities of these particular imaging devices affect patient bodies as objects, instruments and also as subjects of imaging. Besides expanding patients' visual views of their body, imaging devices extend their haptic reach as well. Even before visualizing the body's interior – during an actual examination, that is – technological devices affect how patients feel their body. The patient-spectator of real-time medical images is never a mere spectator, but is always also physically engaged with the object and instrument of visualization – one's own body.

Professional preparations

Imaging devices need an operator to produce meaningful images. Various medical professionals are involved in real-time imaging and in the configuration of a body that is fit for imaging. Imaging and images occupy rather different roles in the work of radiologists and endoscopists. Radiologists are specialists in imaging. Endoscopists are surgeons or gastroenterologists who also perform other examinations and actually treat patients. Except for those working with real-time imaging technologies, radiologists hardly ever see a patient. Images are produced by technicians who then send them to the radiologist for interpretation.

My focus in this section is not on medical professionals' preparations for a singular imaging event, but on the formation of physicians, technicians and nurses into skilled performers of particular types of examinations through professional training.[35] Professionals acquire a bifocal vision: they learn how to see wholes as well as parts and how to relate the different levels. Furthermore, to learn to perform real-time imaging they need to develop visual as well as haptic skills.

---

[35] Some light on such individual preparations will be shed in the next chapter. However, I did not systematically collect information on individual professionals' preparations for particular examinations. The focus during my fieldwork has been on following two actors: patients and images.

A bifocal vision: how medicine constructs visual body-objects

Basic medical training has a strong visual orientation. Images, from anatomical pictures to microscopic visualizations, are central to physicians' professional training in the identification of normalities and abnormalities on and inside patients' bodies. To untrained eyes, most microscopic as well as macroscopic medical images merely show unrecognizable shapes and structures. Candidate physicians, however, acquire a specific visual literacy to 'read' bodies and the devices used to image them.[36]

Like other modes of clinical imaging, radiological and endoscopic vision results from the confrontation of two levels of viewing: reading a full, contextualized body and reading fragmented body parts. Physicians are trained to see and interpret anatomical details of the whole body and to narrow down their vision to assess the pathology of particular parts. Among the principal teaching instruments, we find anatomical atlases showing organs and structures in the context of a whole body-complex. In these atlases, bodies are "made notational" (Prasad 2005: 292), i.e. "converted into sets of isolable, disjoint, and differentiable parts" (idem: 291).

Textbooks used in medical curricula often feature radiological or endoscopic pictures next to anatomical pictures, images made with other (imaging) technologies or similar images of the same or another body. Combinations of schematic, anatomical, or other images provide medical students with a comparative framework for reading medical images, including radiological and endoscopic representations, which merges graphic properties of different types of visualizations. By means of lines, arrows or figures, images are inscribed with particular standards and readings.

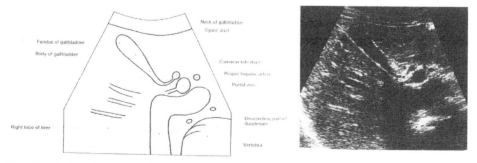

Examples of schematic representations of ultrasound images, from Wicke, L. et al. (eds) (1994), *Atlas of Radiologic Anatomy*. Philadelphia: Lea & Febiger.

---

[36] Cf. (Te Hennepe 2007) on the concept of visual literacy.

The juxtaposition of different types of images of the 'same' object affords the combination of information acquired by various means to identify what is the condition of a particular patient.[37] Thus textbooks as well as anatomical atlases train medical students to acquire a bifocal vision (Prasad 2005: 292). Images acquired by means of various techniques enable the visual distinction of the object of diagnosis situated inside a body. The presentation of images in textbooks and atlases suggests that, even if acquired by different means and sometimes depicting different body parts or structures, each picture ultimately refers to the same object, which is either a generic or a specific patient body. In the next chapter I will argue that the ultimate presentation of the body as a unit obscures that this unity actually results from coordinating multiple phenomena, including X-rays or ultrasound waves, tissues and fluids, blood flows and bowel movements, colors and numbers (cf. Mol 2002).

Real-time imaging differs from many other forms of medical representation because of the simultaneous presence of the whole body under examination and the fragmented representations of that body on the monitor during image production and interpretation. Novice radiologists and endoscopists therefore need to learn how to make, watch and interpret moving images all at the same time. Protocols, guidelines and checklists, such as the list on the next page, originally posted on a cupboard in the ultrasound room, serve as handles.

Quantification organs and tumor size

Aorta:

Determine the maximum AP-exterior diameter measured on a transection. Over 3 centimeters is deviant.

Liver:

Determine the maximum midcalvicular craniocaudal length of the liver on the patient lying on the back. More than 15 centimeter could be an indication for hepatomegaly.

Choledochus:

Measured in the liver hilus. Diameter over 6 mm deviant.

Gallbladder:

Length over 3 cm deviant, diameter over 4 cm deviant. Wall thickness (measured ventrally) over 3 mm deviant.

I have included this list to indicate that medical imaging is as much about *measuring* and the interpretation of *numbers* as it is about *seeing* and the interpretation of *pictures*. Medical

---

[37] I have put 'same' in quotation marks to indicate a constructivist notion of representation rather than the reflective notion implied in this statement.

professionals use imaging in combination with other data collection.[38] The results of an imaging event include visual data as well as numbers taken from measurements (e.g. the size of an organ, a tumor or a cyst) and punctures or biopsies (i.e. samples of bodily fluid or tissue).

Characteristic for real-time imaging is that most of the measuring and interpretation work takes place during the imaging event. Fluoroscopy, ultrasound and endoscopy produce dynamic representations that show the body in action. Still images can be stored and printed during a real-time examination, to be inspected afterwards or for inclusion in textbooks, yet they provide another type of information than real-time images. As real-time images, the pictures only exist while they are made. When still images are stored, moved and combined with other images, the direct link with the material patient body is lost. Although multimedia materials, such as CD-ROMs and websites, are able to show moving pictures, they fail to convey the 'real-timeness' of ultrasound, fluoroscopic or endoscopic pictures.

For the interpretation of still images, physicians acquire an extensive frame of reference through education and working experience. Conventions for imaging, looking and reporting provide them with standard images of a normal body and its possible deviations. For real-time images, however, that visual frame of reference is of limited value, because physicians are not merely interpreters of medical images, but also their producers. To a certain extent, reading images can be learned 'from books'. Making images, however, can only be learned by doing (cf. Pasveer 1992).

Learning by doing: haptic skills in real-time imaging

In a radiology department, most of the training for novice radiologists takes place in the reading room. Supervised by a senior, residents watch pictures on light boxes and computer screens; they describe what they see and compare the images to those in atlases available in the reading room and to images from other examinations. Another important teaching venue is the conference room, where cases and images are presented and discussed by attending

---

[38] The position of imaging and images in the work of radiologists and in the work of physicians performing endoscopies is rather different. Radiologists are specialists in imaging, whereas endoscopy is a common diagnostic and therapeutic tool in some clinical specializations, like surgery or internal medicine. Doctors working in an endoscopy department see and treat patients as well. Radiologists may see and talk to patients during the production and reading of images, but are not involved in their treatment nor do they communicate diagnoses.

physicians, radiologists, residents and students at fixed times every day.[39] Conversely, except for the X-rays and stored still produced during a fluoroscopic examination, ultrasound and fluoroscopic images never make it to the reading room and they seldom appear in the conference room. In the endoscopy unit, there are no such things as reading and conference rooms. Some still images taken from ultrasound, fluoroscopy or endoscopy examinations may be stored or printed and a final report may be postponed until lab results arrive, yet the majority of the images I address in my analysis are read during the examination itself.

Since real-time images are read while they are made, learning how to read them is done while learning how to produce them. Most professional training for radiological or endoscopic imaging occurs on the spot, in actual clinical practice rather than in a classroom. Most of the examinations I observed during my fieldwork in the radiology department, and some in the endoscopy department, were performed by – more or less experienced – residents. The following quote by an experienced surgeon supervising a new resident during one of her first endoscopic examinations illustrates the haptic nature of real-time imaging.[40]

> This I cannot teach you, you have to feel it. This is not something you learn in a correspondence course. It is like cycling, you have to feel for yourself how to steer. (....) You just have to do it, nice instructions do not help. You just have to feel it, and then it comes by itself.

Learning to perform an endoscopy involves the development of visual as well as haptic skills. Like the "knowledge of the object is embodied in the surgeon at the same time that the surgeon brings that object into being" (Prentice 2005: 841) during the training of surgeons, not only the eyes of the novice endoscopist are trained, but her body is as well. Endoscopists as well as radiologists performing an ultrasound or a fluoroscopy get to know the interior of a patient's body by watching a representation that they are producing at the same time. As in surgical practices, the production of a patient's body as an object of visual knowledge in practices of medical imaging involves physicians' hands as much as their eyes (cf. Hirschauer 1991). The coordination of visual and haptic information is key to real-time imaging procedures.[41]

---

[39] For an eloquent and elaborate description of the construction and articulation of radiological gazes in a CT suite, see Saunders (forthcoming).

[40] Haptic includes tactile perception, i.e. perception by means of (exterior) touch, as well as kinaesthetic, interior perception of one's own bodily movement.

[41] The development of endoscopic simulators for the training of novice endoscopists illustrates the technology's haptic nature as well. Simulators consist of a plastic torso with an endoscope entered orally or rectally and a

Whereas X-ray, CT and MRI show a standard, objectified body, readable for everyone who has acquired a professional radiological gaze, real-time images are only meaningful to those who actually made them. The supposed subjectivity of real-time imaging among medical professionals is largely due to the haptic nature of real-time imaging. In their preparations for imaging, professionals learn to anticipate a particular kind of body. It can be passively or actively involved in imaging, yet a patient's body is ultimately presented as an opaque material object in need of visual penetration. That does not mean that patients are exclusively passive objects: they are actively involved in their own objectivation.

Patient preparations

Besides machines and doctors, a real-time imaging event also requires a prepared patient. The first step towards an ultrasound, fluoroscopy or endoscopy is often a visit to the family doctor. If anamnesis and a physical examination do not provide enough information for a diagnosis or therapy, a general practitioner (GP) refers a patient either directly to the Radiology or Endoscopy department for a particular examination or to a specialist for further examination and subsequent referral for imaging if necessary. Some examinations are performed for screening purposes rather than for diagnostic reasons, for instance when a patient has a genetic predisposition or has reached the age where population screening is indicated.

The examinations I observed in the Endoscopy and Radiology departments were mostly common procedures. For many patients, the examination I observed was among the first medical interventions after a visit to their GP.[42] In the Netherlands general practitioners can directly refer a patient for an ultrasound, sigmoidoscopy[43], X-colon[44], Sellinck[45], or

---

monitor showing computer-generated images that react to every move of the endoscope. The simulator makes the performer of an examination feel resistance when trying to pass a virtual twist in the bowel. To make the simulator more real, it can be set to moan in case of pain or gag upon introduction of the scope in the esophagus.

[42] Patients with chronic conditions sometimes can bypass the GP and immediately make an appointment with their attending specialist. In the case of regular check-ups, like a yearly endoscopy to monitor a patient's condition after surgery, patients also set an appointment directly with the department.

[43] Endoscopic examination of the first sixty centimeters of the colon (sigmoid), from the anus upwards.

[44] Fluoroscopic examination of the large intestine (colon), using contrast liquid to visualize the colon using X-rays.

[45] Fluoroscopic examination of the first part of the small intestine (duodenum), using contrast liquid to visualize the duodenum using X-rays.

MCU.[46] These examinations therefore often feature relatively early in a diagnostic trajectory. For other examinations, like a colonoscopy, a specialist's referral is required.

Informed by the media or by their own previous experiences or those of others, some patients who visit a GP or specialist suggest, or even require, a referral for a particular examination. Usually, however, patients do not visit a doctor with the explicit objective to be referred for an ultrasound, fluoroscopy or endoscopy. Whether upon their own request or not, however, the submission of one's body to a medical regime requires the active participation of any patient. Submission to medical requirements implies the objectivation of one's own body and occurs at two levels: physical preparation and information collection.

Preparing one's body

In its natural state, a body may contain substances and fluids that obstruct a technologically mediated view into its interior. A body may also lack matter that provides the contrast that enables a radiologist or endoscopist to distinguish between normality and abnormality. When they are referred for a particular examination, patients usually receive specific instructions. They are required to bring their bodies in a proper condition for imaging. Each examination requires its own particular preparations that start somewhere between a few hours and a few days before the examination. The necessary transformation may merely entail being at the right place at the right time, but some examinations require substantial preparations before any meaningful image can be produced.

Requirements for ultrasound examinations may differ, depending on which body part is the object of visualization.[47] An ultrasound of the kidneys demands no special preparation, but an ultrasound examination of the lower abdomen calls for a full bladder. Since ultrasound can visualize fluid but not air, patients are required to drink one liter of water one hour before the examination. Due to ultrasonic impenetrability of air, patients are not allowed to eat or drink any gas-inducing products, such as onions and carbonated drinks, from the day before an ultrasound of the upper abdomen. From a few hours before the examination, eating, drinking or smoking is not permitted at all.

---

[46] Fluoroscopic examination of the kidneys and bladder, using contrast liquid to visualize the filling and emptying of the bladder.

[47] Preparatory requirements described here may vary among hospitals. Elsewhere, patients may be required to keep a diet for a longer (or shorter) period of time, have another variety of food and drinks or take a different kind of laxative.

Intestinal examinations by means of fluoroscopy require patients to refrain from eating two days prior to the examination, and to drink lots of clear liquids until the night before the examination, after which eating, drinking or smoking is no longer permitted. Moreover, the intestines must be cleaned by taking laxatives, which make stools loose and stimulate peristaltic movements, causing considerable discomfort and frequent toilet visits. For a fluoroscopic inspection of the stomach, patients need to consume effervescent powder and a contrast substance immediately before the examination.

Although there are differences,[48] preparations for sigmoidoscopies and colonoscopies are comparable to the preparations for a fluoroscopic examination of the colon. Many patients have a hard time preparing for an endoscopic bowel examination. The frequent defecation induced by laxatives makes it necessary to be close to a toilet all the time, necessitating many patients to take a day off from work or school. Besides by frequent and sometimes painful passing of stool, patients are troubled by the amount of liquid intake required and by the foul-tasting fluid laxative. Especially the intake of three liters of salty lavage fluid within three hours, required for a colonoscopy, is hard for many people. A patient who already had problems keeping her weight up told me that preparing for a colonoscopy cost her two kilograms, which she did not regain. The combination of drinking laxative fluids and fasting makes some patients nauseated, weak, irritable and prone to headaches.

Preparations that transform bodies into compliant objects for real-time imaging also inform those bodies as objects and subjects of patients' perceptions and experience. Patients do not perceive their interior body visually yet – as they will during the real-time imaging examination – but they feel how it is being affected by a diet and by laxatives. Draining the body or filling it with unnatural substances cause physical and emotional discomfort, and affect the body as an object of a patient's sensory perception. Preparations affect how patients imagine their inner bodies. Preparations often trigger emotions connected to one's body as well, such as anxiety about the eventual results or memories of previous examinations or illness episodes.

Preparing for imaging is a form of 'active dispossession' (cf. Gomart and Hennion 1999): patients are actively involved in transforming their bodies from their everyday state into an extraordinary state of potential visibility. In order to comply with the conditions of the imaging apparatus – consisting of imaging device, physician and body - patients are required

---

[48] For a sigmoidoscopy it takes only one day of not eating, drinking a lot, and purging. Furthermore, on the day of the examination in the hospital, it is completed by a clysma. For a colonoscopy, the regime is similar, but takes longer: a patient must refrain from eating for two days and is supposed to drink an additional three liters of liquid for lavage of the colon. No clysma is then required.

to do things they would rather not and refrain from activities they usually enjoy. While they translate a body into an object of medical visualization, preparations for real-time imaging affect the body that is an object of a patient's sensory perceptions, emotions and reflections as well. What is more, they transform patients' agency, perception and experience. Preparations allow a particular subject to emerge: a patient who perceives his or her body in unprecedented ways and experiences a body that is usually absent from conscious experience (cf. Leder 1990). Medical imaging affects a patient body long before any machine has entered the scene. Patients' preparations for real-time imaging illustrate how embodiment is both a mode of objectivity as well as a subjective state of being.

Collecting information

> *You lie down on your left side. The endoscope is inserted via the anus into the large intestine and is carefully moved upwards. The moving of the tube, during which some air is inflated into the intestine as well, may cause cramps in the abdomen. These cramps usually disappear when the tube is slowly pulled backwards. The intestinal mucus is carefully inspected, if necessary tissue samples are taken. In most cases we can tell directly after the examination whether abnormalities were found. If tissue samples have to be sent to the Pathology laboratory, results will be sent to the requesting physician who can discuss them with you after one to two weeks. In case you are troubled by gas after the examination, a visit to the toilet usually provides relief.*
>
> Quote from patient information flyer on sigmoidoscopy

> *During this examination you will be lying on a table. A small tube is guided through your mouth or nose via your stomach to the small intestine. A contrast substance is administered through this tube; this is necessary to visualize the small intestine. Then a number of pictures are taken. The examination takes about one hour, depending on how fast your bowels work. During the examination you wear a disposable paper apron.*
>
> Quote from patient information flyer about fluoroscopy of the small intestine

> *A small tube is guided via the urethra to the bladder. Through this tube the bladder is filled with contrast fluid. During the filling and emptying of the bladder pictures are*

taken. During the examination you wear a disposable paper apron. The examination takes about half an hour.
Quote from patient information flyer about fluoroscopy of the bladder.

During an ultrasound the organs in the body are visualized by sound waves (which you cannot hear). A small machine sends and receives those sound waves and scans the skin. To optimize contact, a kind of jelly is put on the skin. NO X-rays are used. The examination is painless. An ultrasound examination takes about twenty minutes.
Quote from patient information flyer about ultrasound

The above quotes are taken from information flyers preparing patients for various real-time imaging examinations. Patients usually receive information on the procedure through written or verbal instructions from the referring physician or from the desk personnel making the appointment. Patients are addressed as owners of bodies ("The examination takes about one hour, depending on how fast your bowels work") as well as subjects of sensory perception ("the examination is not painful") and purposeful action ("If after the examination you are troubled by gas, a visit to the toilet usually provides relief"). Brochures also describe the need for preparation and hold patients co-responsible for the success of an imaging event. An endoscopy flyer, for example, states that in rare cases an endoscope may cause perforation of the intestine, yet thorough cleaning of the colon by the patient taking laxatives reduces that risk. Flyers provide information on the general purpose and procedures of an examination, on its duration, on the area of investigation, on possible complications and on the aftermath of an examination, including the communication of results. Patients are encouraged to ask questions and all brochures provide a telephone number for further inquiries.

Patients' organizations publish information on examinations and imaging procedures as well.[49] On websites, for example, they discuss possibilities to make an endoscopic examination less embarrassing by choosing a comfortable position and to make it less painful by asking for sedation. They also provide flyers on specific diseases and examinations with information on the body part to be imaged, the technology being used, the possible problems it helps diagnose, possible interventions performed during an examination, alternative examinations, preparations, the course of an examination and its risks, and possible pain and discomfort. Information from patient organizations serves a different purpose than hospital

---

[49] For example the Dutch Crohn Colitis Ulcerosa Association (http://www.crohn-colitis.nl) and the Stomach Liver Bowel Foundation (Maag Lever Darm Stichting, http://www.mlds.nl)

brochures. Whereas hospital flyers aim to prepare patient bodies for imaging machines, information from patient organizations emphasizes physical and emotional coping procedures for patients. Hospital flyers address patients as managers of their own interior bodies, whereas patient organizations primarily consider patients as persons with physical and emotional feelings.

Hospital flyers for colon fluoroscopy and colonoscopy mention the use of sedatives, relaxing the intestines, yet also temporarily rendering a patient less conscious, prohibiting their ability to drive a car for several hours after the examination. Brochures emphasize the relaxing effect of medication and most patients expect to be unconscious or semi-conscious during an examination. In the next chapter, I describe how sedatives may affect patients differently. Some patients fall asleep, whereas others are aware of what happens; some patients are able to react to the doctor's questions and instructions, verbally as well as physically, and can watch the live, moving pictures on the monitor during most of the examination.

This last feature, the possibility for patients to watch the monitor during an examination, is never mentioned in any flyer, although the possibility to watch live images of one's own interior does feature in the illustrations of some patient organizations' brochures.

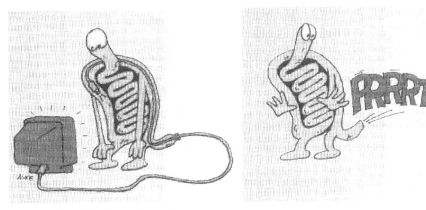

Illustrations from MLD flyer on sigmoidoscopy

Neither hospital flyers nor those by patients' organizations mention what the images might actually show, why a particular technology can or cannot visualize particular body parts and organs or how particular preparations improve the quality of the images. Flyers inform patients about what they ought to do in order to make the machines visualize their interior, but they do not anticipate patients' own potential spectatorship. They present the need for patients to actively engage in the transformation of their bodies and anticipate what they will feel and do during an examination, yet do not prepare them for what they will see.

Doctors and patients get their information on real-time imaging from different sources. Doctors regard images as a possible source of data and use them to exclude possible diagnoses, rather than to establish a diagnosis. The presence of gallstones, for instance, is sometimes not directly visible, but can be inferred from the dilatation of a bile duct visualized by ultrasound. Many physicians claim that patients expect an examination to result in a diagnosis and subsequent possibilities for treatment. They expect too much, since in the case of medical imaging, what you see is not what you get. In light of the clinical setting, including the flyers, it is hard to see what should temper their expectations. By obscuring the practices of looking and emphasizing physical processes, flyers contribute to the cultural discourse of a 'transparent body' and of imaging as 'seeing what is wrong' (cf. Van Dijck 2005).

Patients' physical as well as their mental preparations for a real-time imaging event actively engage them in the objectivation of their own body. Preparations also contribute to the formation of a particular subject position:[50] the position of patients as managers of their own bodies. Although patients in many cases will be spectators of the real-time images produced during an examination, they are not explicitly being prepared for that role. Patients are not alerted that in the cause of preparations, they are transformed into an object that is rather different from their usual body. Patients' own preparations of their body for imaging results in expectations that professionals deem unrealistic. In the next chapter we will meet several patients who believe that during a real-time imaging event they – or at least the doctor, who has been trained for it – can see what is inside their body. However, a doctor can only see something thanks to an accurately orchestrated composition of elements.

Paper work: request forms as coordination devices

Notes pinned up on the wall of the central ultrasound office familiarize inexperienced radiologists with standards for ultrasound measurements of particular organs as well as with guidelines for the layout of an ultrasound report. Hospital flyers present to patients the standard order of an examination. Guidelines for the use of imaging machines indicate how equipment should be used in order to produce meaningful images. Detailed digital protocols

---

[50] Michel Foucault has coined the notion of 'subject position' to describe that what a subject can do or say follows from its position in a particular discursive and institutional context (Foucault 1972 (1969)).

for nurses and administrators aim at patients' active compliance with imaging requirements. All such 'papers' are means to orchestrate the collective body in anticipation of real-time imaging. Individual preparations for an examination by imaging machines, professional imagers and patients are guided by implicit or explicit standards attached to a certain job or a particular piece of equipment. Such guidelines contribute to the enactment of particular bodies alongside such standards. Protocols, guidelines, patient files and records – increasingly digitalized – are benchmarks in the various actors' work done to produce meaningful images.

Of particular importance in the preparatory phase of imaging are request forms, coordinating the actors that have been introduced in this chapter's previous sections into an apparatus fit for real-time imaging. Every real-time imaging examination starts with a standard request form completed by the referring physician or the hospital's diagnostic center. It is patients' passport to the radiology or endoscopy department. Except in emergency cases and for particular follow-up examinations, patients cannot make an appointment without a request form. Standard request forms are at the disposal of all physicians working in a clinical department. Patients referred by a physician outside the hospital need to exchange their referral notes for the standard hospital form at the diagnostic center. This center is a gatekeeper, providing patients with the right key for access to certain diagnostic and therapeutic facilities. At the diagnostic center the information provided by the referring doctor is translated into the categories listed on the form: the name of the requesting physician and her or his department, date of the request, type of examination requested, indication and question the examination should address, other relevant clinical data, and the date of the last examination the patient had in the same department. Different forms are used for the radiology and the endoscopy department, yet the categories largely correspond. The endoscopy form includes more specific categories about the patient's condition (use of medication, presence of or therapy for blood coagulation problems, other specific measures required), whereas the radiology form leaves some room for the radiologist to write down remarks during the examination.

The categorized information on the request form presents a fragmented body. Divided into possible objects of visualization, the body appears as a potential source of data that can be compared to other data in order to identify the normality or abnormality of the body's medical condition. The present section describes the categorization of patients' bodies and the work that is involved in the translation of complaints and of symptoms diagnosed by a doctor into an indication for a particular examination.

Bodies in categories

Sifting through a request form yields a lot of information on the translation of a patient's body into an object of medical imaging. By means of electronic or paper records, doctors are informed about a particular part of patients' pasts, thus allowing for medical continuities, yet losing sight of illness as it is embedded in patients' lives. In the endoscopy department, the performing physician receives a paper record, including the most recent request form. The record contains all request forms and reports of endoscopic examinations undergone by patients in this hospital. New requests and reports are put in front of the previous ones. The first page of the file consists of a chronological list of all examinations. In the radiology department, patients' records are electronically accessible from any computer terminal in the department. With a few clicks, a doctor has access to a chronological list of radiological and endoscopic examinations a patient has had and to reports of all those examinations, unless they have been performed before 1990. Flipping or clicking through a patient's record, doctors can easily travel through patients' histories of examinations in their department.

It is relevant to distinguish the origin of a request form. Patients cannot request examinations themselves. They are referred by their general practitioner, their attending physician from one of the hospital's outpatient's clinics or wards, the Emergency Room physician, or a physician from another hospital. The name and location of the physician who requested the examination usually provides quite some information on the history of the request. A request filed by a general practitioner, for example, is often one of the first steps towards identifying illness or health. In such cases, it is not clear what to look for and what to expect, neither for the imaging physician, nor for the patient.

If a general practitioner suspects a problem in a patient's colon, he or she can either refer the patient to a specialist for further anamnesis or immediately request a sigmoidoscopy, an endoscopic inspection of the last sixty centimeters of the colon.[51] General practitioners are not allowed to request colonoscopies, examinations of the entire colon. Some sigmoidoscopies therefore are requested as a 'first step' that is likely to be followed by a colonoscopy. Patients then need to prepare for an examination twice, whereas a specialist might have decided to perform a colonoscopy in the first place.

The history of seemingly similar requests may result in outcomes that affect patient bodies rather differently. Since surgeons and gastroenterologists have their own distinct ways

---

[51] The specialist may be a surgeon or a gastroenterologist, depending on the suspected nature of the problem.

of performing endoscopies it is particularly relevant who requests and performs an endoscopic examination.[52] The suspected nature of the problem leads a general practitioner to refer a patient to either a surgeon or a gastroenterologist.[53] When patients are referred for an endoscopy by a surgeon, the examination will also be performed by a surgeon. The same goes for gastroenterologists: they only request examinations from their colleagues. That is not due to nepotism, but to the suspected nature of a problem: surgical problems should be solved by surgeons, gastroenterological ones by gastroenterologists.

Central on a request form are the type of examination requested and the question it should address. Different technologies are used to depict different things: X-rays and CT are good for visualizing solid structures, ultrasound and MRI are particularly apt for imaging soft tissues. There is a hierarchy among radiological imaging technologies. An assistant in the radiology department told me: "It seems that patients are referred for an ultrasound on any suspicion. First ultrasound, then a CT, then a MRI, that is the order. They start with a shower of shot." Among the imaging technologies able to visualize soft tissue, ultrasound is often the first to be applied: it is relatively cheap, fast, and relatively 'non-invasive'. CT and MRI images, however, are generally considered to be more accurate and objective, since their interpretation is not inextricably bound up with their production.

From a specific preliminary diagnosis or indication the choice for a particular examination logically follows. Some problems can be made visible with a particular technology, but not with another. For a check-up of the colon after the removal of polyps, for example, a colonoscopy should be requested. To measure the size of polycystic kidneys, an ultrasound is the examination to request. Many of the examinations performed in the radiology and endoscopy department, however, are not guided by such specific questions. Although not always the first step, imaging often starts off a diagnostic trajectory. General complaints such as abdominal pain can have innumerable causes. Based on anamnesis, physical examination and sometimes urine tests, blood tests or other diagnostic instruments, a physician usually develops some idea of what might be the cause of the problems before deciding upon the most appropriate visualization technique. The choice for a particular examination brings along a specific set-up for an imaging machine, a certain scope of medical interpretation and definite requirements for patients.

---

[52] E.g. sedation is more common in endoscopies performed by gastroenterologists than in surgical inspections.
[53] Unlike for a radiological examination, for an endoscopy the requesting physician can be the one who performs the actual examination. A physician then knows the patient and his or her particularities and potential complexities.

On the request form, the examinations are not described merely as 'ultrasound', 'fluoroscopy', or 'endoscopy', but specified in terms of the specific area or part of the body to be visualized. The object of examination is a fragment of a body rather than a whole. For example, referring doctors may request an ultrasound examination of the liver, the bladder or the right kidney, which are then translated by the diagnostic center or the personnel of the radiology department into examinations of the 'upper abdomen' or 'lower abdomen'. Each specific examination has its own inbuilt settings in an imaging machine. For an ultrasound of the upper abdomen, for example, different parameters are selected than for an ultrasound of the kidneys, in terms of scope and contrast. The interior body is constructed as an object of imaging that gets recontextualized when it moves from one clinical space to another. Radiological or endoscopic categorizations may eclipse those of the requesting physician. I observed the endoscopic examination of a patient's sigmoid, performed by a gastroenterologist. Upon his arrival in the examination room, the nurse noticed that the examination was indicated for hemorrhoids. The gastroenterologist then decided that the patient had to come back for an examination by a surgeon – who was not available at the time – because a surgeon would not only be able to diagnose the likely cause of his problems but would treat it as well. Physicians require some idea about the nature of the patient's problem in order to decide who should perform a particular examination. If that is not clear, patients suffer the consequences. The patient with hemorrhoids, who did prepare for the sigmoidoscopy by means of a diet and laxatives, was sent back home and another appointment was made.

The indication, i.e. the symptoms or preliminary diagnosis underlying a request for a particular examination, constitutes a separate category on the request form. Whereas a physician can only choose from a limited number of examinations for visualizing parts of the inner body, the 'indication' or 'question' category on the request form has a wider scope. The guiding question for an examination is complemented by other relevant clinical data if deemed necessary by the requesting physician. In their articulation of the question, physicians anticipate the standard report of an examination. Usually, however, a requesting doctor is not so much interested in a patient body's correspondence to a standard body, but in its deviations from it. That is why attending physicians are often interested in results or images that are not included in the standard scope of an examination. During fluoroscopic examinations, for example, standard images are produced at fixed points in time, e.g. before filling up the bladder with contrast fluid (MCU), or while releasing the rectum (defaecogram). If requesting physicians want to know about other body parts or moments, they need to indicate that on the request form. Usually, specialists from the hospital will be more aware of such standards than general practitioners. General practitioners, however, also have their standardized ways of interpreting, classifying and reporting an anamnesis (cf. Timmermans and Berg 2003). Thus, although the *question* category seems to leave more room for doctors' free expression than the category of *requested examination* does, framing a question always entails very specific translations of a patient's story and physical matter – translations that are highly standardized and standardizing.

Translation, multiplication, coordination: the work of request forms

Request forms translate patients into textual, standardized and fragmented objects. Their bodies are distributed among departments, specializations and physicians, who divide them into relevant and irrelevant areas and parts and who classify a body according to general criteria. It is transformed from a lived body "into a juxtaposition of organs, parameters, rows of numbers, graphs, and so forth" (Berg and Bowker 1997: 514). A request for imaging does not straightforwardly result in images of interior body parts, but materially reconfigures that body by directing what will happen, where it will be touched, and what it needs to do. This is an example of 'alignment convergence' (Bowker 1994: 46) of the request form and the body it represents: the request form inscribes its categories and classifications on the body it seems to represent (cf. Berg and Bowker 1997: 519). The body that is the site for diagnostic or therapeutic visualization is thus the product of what the request form does: framing the setting for a diagnostic or therapeutic intervention by coordinating the work of the various actors.

Request forms convey information on the trajectory of which a planned examination is part. That trajectory is a network of examinations and medical interactions that includes a patient's anamnesis. An analysis of request forms exemplifies how "the categories used in discussing health conditions are shaped" (Mol & Berg 1998: 1) in networks of patients' bodies, physicians and imaging technologies. A request only works when it is related to other actors, introduced earlier in this chapter: patient bodies, doctors, machines, guidelines and protocols. Connected to a variety of human and non-human actors, request forms "constitute the network, or the dispositif, within which the body acquires its specific ontology" (Berg and Bowker 1997: 514). Although request forms present fragmented bodies, they undoubtedly also refer to a single body. In the words of Annemarie Mol, they constitute a *body multiple* (Mol 2002).

Their recontextualization into diagnostic practices renders objectified body fragments part of new wholes. A request form inscribes a patient's body with a particular history, linking past and present conditions and examinations. Request forms render bodies comparable as bearers of textbook diseases and yet they preserve some of the patients' particularities, not only by including their name and date of birth. Requests forms present not mere body parts, but also persons. On the request form for a colonoscopy of a young woman with Crohn's disease, for example, the requesting physician indicates that good sedation is necessary, since the woman has been terrified by previous examinations. Another example is an ultrasound request stating "C2H5OH" in the question area of the form. The chemical formula for ethanol indicates that the patient in question has an alcohol problem.

Request forms coordinate the embodied, materially heterogeneous work involved in preparing bodies as objects and subjects of real-time imaging. The choice for a certain examination and the phrasing of the question aims at translating what can be felt in something that can be seen. A sigmoidoscopy request, for example, aims at translating abdominal pain and rectal blood loss into a visible cause, like polyps or hemorrhoids. The request form coordinates the anticipated visible body with other medical bodies, enacted by words (anamnesis), touch (physical examination) or other visualizations (e.g. microscopic images). Thus request forms contribute to the robustness of a body's visible interior that machines, doctors and patients prepare for.

Collective embodiment and the enactment of disease and illness

Actor-network theory provides a method and vocabulary to describe a body's preparation for real-time imaging as a material-semiotic process of collective embodiment: a matter of meaning as well as a matter of matter (cf. Barad 2003). We have come a long way from the painful belly of Mr. Bergmans in chapter 2 to a body-collective of doctors, patients, machines, and request forms now.

Particular assemblies of machines, bodies, physicians and forms provide all actors involved with specific abilities to act. In the present chapter, I have described how various elements, which enable patients to act and perceive during an examination and which enable images to appear, already get connected before an actual examination takes place. Patients' bodies are composed into competent 'bodies-for-imaging' in various preparing practices that come together in an examination room at the time of a real-time imaging event. In this process of composition, patients appear in multiple modes: as potential objects of visualization, as potential spectators and as actors managing their own body. Patients are actively involved in the transformation of their own bodies into objects of imaging and – although less explicitly so – into prospective spectators of images of their interior. They subject themselves to a regime of physical preparations and information to align their bodies with machines and physicians. The body that patients act *upon* is materially resistant, yet adaptable; it is opaque, yet potentially visible. The body they act *with* is capable of sensory perception, communication, emotion and cognition.

The preparations of bodies by imaging devices, doctors, patients and request forms condition bodies for real-time imaging. Preparations constitute processes of objectivation as well as subjectivation of patients' bodies, including their state of health or illness. What gets articulated in the production and operation of imaging machines, training of physicians, preparations of patient bodies and categorizations of request forms, is what anthropologists usually describe as *disease*: a potential attribute of bodies and a prospective object of medical diagnosis and therapy. Simultaneously, real-time imaging preparations inscribe patients' bodies with potential *illness*: the word used by anthropologist to describe patients' subjective experience of their embodied condition. Illness is a subjective experience that may be linked to a disease once it is connected to technology and professional medical expertise. Yet from the moment a patient's experiencing and experienced body meets the physician's objectified image of a body, the development of both modes of embodiment is interconnected and the distinction between illness and disease that is central to medical anthropology, actually looses its descriptive and analytical power.

During a body's preparation for real-time imaging, illness/disease is enacted as a phenomenon that is both discursive and material (cf. Barad 1998: 105, 2003: 816). As summarized in the conceptual matrix in chapter 2: 'bodies are articulated in networks of humans and non-humans' and 'disease emerges from hybrid configurations of actors, including patients' bodies'. In the present chapter I have argued that the enactment of disease involves embodied experience as much as techno-medical knowledge. The production of medical knowledge starts (long) before physician and patient meet during an examination.

Patients' embodied experience is one of its constituents. Others are the normal body to which physicians compare a patient's body, the standardized, equipped body that an imaging device is set up for and the fragmented body anticipated on a request form. In the build-up to the examination the experiencing and experienced patient's body meets these other bodies. Connections are made that result in the emergence of a body that is fit for imaging – or not.

4   Moving pictures: productions of presence in real-time imaging events

On the examination table lies a patient. She watches the radiology assistant who sets the machine for an ultrasound examination of her lower abdomen. Somewhere in another room, waiting for the gastroenterologist to come in and start the endoscopic examination of his colon, a patient watches indefinable grey contours on a monitor. At some other place in the hospital, a patient in a green apron feels burpy after taking the effervescent powder that should fill her stomach with air in order to make it visible for the radiologist, who can come in and start the fluoroscopic examination any time. In a few minutes, the bodies of those patients on the examination tables will also appear as moving pictures on the monitors next to them. They are ready for action.

Herein lies the origin of the fascination that triggered this book: in the examination, a real-time imaging event that produces visual representations of parts of patients' interior bodies while patients themselves are watching. There is the aura of transparency, of immediacy, of direct access to one's own body on the one hand, and the technological transformation and complex reading on the other. The present chapter describes how bodies are translated into real-time images. It explores the conditions of technologically mediated illness experience: the various ways in which patients' bodies and real-time images are connected during medical imaging events.

In the previous chapter I described the process of collective embodiment that precedes an imaging event. The bodies that are translated into real-time images are composites. What a body is and what images are is different for each of its constituents: a patient, a physician, a nurse, a technician, a machine. Differences are not merely a matter of interpretation and meaning, but of materiality as well. To address some particular material and perceptual characteristics that distinguish *real-time* images from other medical representations of bodies, like medical files, request forms and printed or still pictures, one needs a specific vocabulary. First, real-time images are evanescent: they appear instantly upon acquisition and they disappear immediately afterwards. Second, the object of real-time medical imaging – a patient's body – is present as a spectator of the images' appearance and is actively involved in their production. Based on my observations of real-time imaging events and on the conceptual frameworks from anthropology, phenomenology and science and technology studies introduced in chapter 2, the present chapter develops a vocabulary to describe the particularities of real-time medical imaging.

The chapter starts with three elaborate case stories. We enter examination rooms during examinations and come to know about both the evanescence and the inescapability of real-time images. The stories indicate that, despite their similarities, real-time imaging events produce a variety of body-image connections. In the second section, I describe four categories of connection, or modes of attachment. They include professional real-time reading of images as well as patients' perceptions, actions and emotions. In the third section the specificities of real-time-ness will be connected to the four modes of attachment by introducing the concept of *presence*. I conclude with a preliminary assessment of the value of my analysis for an understanding of illness experience.

Of bodies and images in real-time

Mr. Coenen's ultrasonic kidneys

Mr. Coenen, whom we have met before in chapter 2, lies on the examination table in an ultrasound room. Diagnosed with polycystic kidney disease almost twenty years ago, he has recently entered a medical trajectory preparing for dialysis and, ultimately, a kidney transplant. He is now in his early fifties, and over the years his condition has gradually deteriorated. The increasing number and size of cysts in his kidneys causes hypertension, bloating, fatigue, and decreasing physical stamina. Today's ultrasound of the abdomen and kidneys is one in a series of examinations to assess whether he is eligible for dialysis once it is indicated by a certain blood value.

The ultrasound room is scarcely lit. Next to the examination table, there is a monitor with a control panel. Mr. Coenen, on the table, has undressed his upper body, his bare chest covered by a towel. His right arm put behind his head, as the radio diagnostics assistant asked him to, he watches the assistant setting the machine for the examination. As soon as an assistant radiologist enters the room, the diagnostics assistant leaves. The radiologist looks at the request form and while glossing over Mr. Coenen's medical situation, takes an ultrasound probe from its holder and applies some gel.

Placed on Mr. Coenen's abdomen, the transducer probe transmits high-frequency sound pulses, which enter his body and bounce back as soon as they hit boundaries between tissues that absorb different amounts of sound waves: kidney tissue and liquid-filled cysts, for example. The probe picks up reflections of waves when they have reached a boundary. The machine measures the time of each echo's return and calculates distances from probe to boundaries. The two-dimensional images that appear on the monitor display the distances and intensities of the reflections.

The monitor hardly shows its first grayish images when Mr. Coenen asks: *"Are those the kidneys you see?"* "Yes, all those black follicles are cysts", the radiologist responds. *"And the light pieces are what is still ok?"* "That is the kidney center". Both the radiologist and Mr. Coenen watch the moving pictures of his right kidney on screen. Occasionally, the radiologist pushes a button to store a digital still image of a large cyst for future reference. "Let me look to the other side", the radiologist says. Mr. Coenen asks whether he needs to turn. " No, just stay like this", the radiologist replies. To see the other kidney, she moves the transducer to the left side of the lower abdomen. She types something on the keyboard of the machine's control panel. The word 'left' appears left of the image on the monitor. *"Is it worse than the other side?"* Mr. Coenen asks. "Hard to say, it is difficult to quantify. Can you hold your breath for a moment?"

Using the mouse attached to the machine's CPU, the radiologist moves a pointer across the screen. By clicking the mouse, she freezes the image. She marks the outline of the black circle.

"What is this?"

"Another cyst."

"A big one, isn't it?"

With another mouse-click, the cyst is 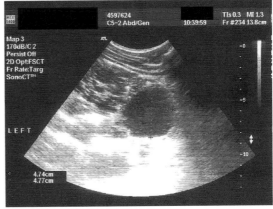 measured. Its size appears in the lower left corner of the image on the monitor. It is indeed the largest cyst measured during this examination. The radiologist stores the image by pressing another button. She applies what she has learned about the specific grammar of dynamic, moving images (cf. Ihde 2003: 17) by training and experience: how to produce a meaningful image of a kidney, how to identify a black circle as a large cyst, how to measure it and compare its appearance and size to normal images and values, and which images to store for future reference or for the patient's record.

While Mr. Coenen alternately holds his breath and breathes normally, he feels the transducer across his abdomen and watches the shifting shapes, words and numbers on the monitor. They show something that he has never seen, yet with which he is so familiar: his illness. Mr. Coenen watches the monitor attentively and asks questions to understand what he sees. Thus he comes to share the radiologist's reading of the images, most of which only exist for the duration of the examination. The transducer moves up a bit, to show the liver as the doctor explains. "I also see some cysts here," the doctor says. "Don't worry, it is quite normal. When you have a disposition for cysts, you can have them everywhere. There are not many, and you do not have any complaints, do you?" No, he has not, Mr. Coenen replies. "Ok, that was it then", the doctor says. "Goodbye."

After Mr. Coenen has left the examination room, the radiologist goes straight to the dictation machine in the department office and dictates the report of the examination. The pictures stored during the examination can be retrieved from a digital storage system and watched on a large monitor in the office.[54] Pictures are only retrieved occasionally and the radiologist who examined Mr. Coenen does not use the storage system at all. She reports from memory and from the few notes she took during the examination.

A fluoroscopic view of Mrs. Vermeulen's bladder

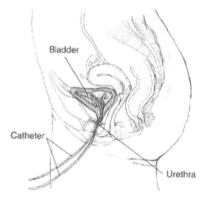

Because of chronic infections of the urinary tract and frequent lower abdominal pain, Mrs. Vermeulen has been scheduled for a micturating cysto-urogram (MCU). The purpose of the fluoroscopic examination is to find out whether her bladder fully empties when she urinates, as remaining urine could be the source of infection. The images produced during an MCU result from the transmission of

Bladder catheterization
http://kidney.niddk.nih.gov/kudiseases/pubs/urodynamic/

---

[54] With this system, the ultrasound unit went ahead of many other radiology and hospital departments, where digital storing systems for images had not yet been introduced. It would be interesting to see how the digital storage of medical images, which increasingly is becoming common practice in Dutch hospitals, has affected, and will further affect, practices of reading real-time images. It might be that the necessity of real-time reading decreases, and that the production and reading of images will become more distributed over time, space and people.

attenuated X-ray beams through a patient's body and appear on two monitors: one situated next to Mrs. Vermeulen and one in the control area of the room, separated from the examination area by a window.

The radiologist explains to Mrs. Vermeulen how her bladder will be filled with contrast fluid through a catheter. To produce diagnostically useful images the bladder needs to be filled to its maximum. The doctor cannot see what that maximum is and needs Mrs. Vermeulen to tell her when her bladder is full. At that point, Mrs. Vermeulen will be asked to urinate in a special bag the radiology assistant shows her. Both the process of filling and of emptying of the bladder will be imaged. The radiologist inserts the catheter, attaches it to a tube and fixes it to a bottle filled with iodine-base contrast. The assistant turns off the light and starts the flow of contrast fluid. The monitors show images of Mrs. Vermeulen's lower abdomen. At the center, slowly a black spot appears: the filling bladder.

Both monitors – the one in front of the radiologist in the control area, and the one next to Mrs Vermeulen – only show real-time images when the radiologist turns on the fluoroscope. During those periods, which last between several seconds to a few minutes, the radiologist stores some still images with a click on the device's control panel, into a digital file for future reference. Moreover, during the examination she takes some standard X-ray pictures according to the MCU protocol, e.g. of the urinary tract before insertion of contrast, and of the full and empty bladder. Those regular X-ray pictures are printed, and of better quality than stored fluoroscopic images. However, they cost more in terms of radiation, time and money.

Mrs. Vermeulen watches the monitor. "You can see for yourself", the radiologist says. When after ten minutes the bottle of contrast fluid is empty, the assistant fixes another 200cc bottle to the machine. When that one is empty as well, she asks Mrs. Vermeulen whether she is still okay. "*I feel some urge, but I can hold it, no problem*". The black spot on the monitor continues to grow bigger. The radiologist tells Mrs. Vermeulen again to signal when she feels "as if you are about to burst, that you can just barely manage to hold it."

While Mrs. Vermeulen feels the contrast fluid filling up her bladder, she alternately watches the monitor, the emptying bottle of contrast fluid, the radiology assistant next to her, and the radiologist behind the window. Halfway during the third bottle, Mrs. Vermeulen's toes start to move. The radiologist explains to the intern that this reflex signals that the bladder is almost full. Yet Mrs. Vermeulen does not object to having another bottle, a 50cc one this time. "Are you going to break the record?" the radiologist asks her jokingly. Mrs.

Vermeulen wants to know: "*How much do you usually give people?*" "To an adult?", the radiologist replies. "Usually two or three bottles."

The fourth bottle finishes quickly. For the radiologist, the sight of the large black spot on the monitor combined with the number of empty bottles triggers a sensory perception. "I almost have to pee myself when I see this", the radiologist whispers to the intern. Yet Mrs. Vermeulen seems okay. She does not know what a full bladder normally looks like. Unlike the radiologist, she has not learned to relate what the monitor shows to what her body feels, or should feel. It is the radiologist who notifies her about such a relation.

Another 50cc bottle is installed, and again it is finished within a few minutes. Since there are only cold bottles of the contrast fluid - iodine - left, the radiologist decides to add 100cc of saline water. Mrs. Vermeulen asks: "*Can I pee now?*" "You have a serious urge?" "*Yes.*" "800cc", the radiologist jots down on the request form. To obtain useful information, the radiologist cannot depend on the pictures alone. She also needs Mrs. Vermeulen's indication of how she feels. The body of Mrs. Vermeulen is not merely the referent for the images, it also indicates the start of the next phase in the examination.

The radiologist asks Mrs. Vermeulen to lie down with her legs straight and then turn to her left and right side, to have bladder pictures taken. Then the assistant removes the catheter and hands her the plastic bag. The examination table is put upright. "Yes, you can pee now". The monitor shows a black stream. From her present position, Mrs. Vermeulen cannot watch it herself. "If you think it is empty, let me know", the assistant tells the patient. A few instants later, Mrs. Vermeulen says she is ready. The examination is over. While the radiologist flips through the stored images behind the control panel, Mrs. Vermeulen gets up and leaves the examination room, about 45 minutes after having entered it. The radiologist behind the control panel glances through the stored images on the monitor. They confirm her reading of the real-time images: there is no urine reflux.

Endoscopic inspections of Mrs. den Hartog's large intestine

In endoscopy room 4, Mrs. den Hartog lies on the examination table, the lower part of her body partly covered by a towel. She is scheduled for a sigmoidoscopy: an inspection of the first sixty centimeters of the large intestine. Mrs. den Hartog is in her mid-forties and regularly suffers from abdominal pain and increasingly frequent bowel movements. She is worried because the pain reminds her of her father's illness, who died of colon cancer a few years ago. Her general practitioner first referred her for a gynecological ultrasound. When this appeared to be normal, a sigmoidoscopy was scheduled.

Lying on her left side, Mrs. den Hartog faces a monitor. It shows images transmitted to a video processor by the lens of the video cable inside a flexible tube, which also contains a light, a channel to transmit air and water, and a channel for the passage of small surgical instruments (e.g. for biopsies). The monitor shows grayish images of the endoscopy room from the viewpoint of the endoscope in the hands of the assisting nurse.

The nurse dims the light in the examination room. The doctor smoothens the endoscope with a lubricant to facilitate the insertion of the tube and to ease some of the patient's discomfort when the endoscope enters. Standing behind the patient, the doctor enters the scope into the anus and guides the flexible tube through the patient's intestines. She pushes a button on the control head of the endoscope to blow air into the intestine. While the endoscope passes from outside to inside her body, Mrs. den Hartog watches the monitor and sees how the grey contours of the imaging room and the outside of her own body give way to moving color images of fleshy, moist structures. The air unfolds the bowel, providing a clear view of the intestinal lumen. "It may cause cramps", the assisting nurse explains to Mrs. den Hartog. "You can just let it pass, it is odorless, it is just clean air that we blow in".

The endoscope does not enter easily. The doctor tries to adjust its position. "*Ouch,*" Mrs. den Hartog calls out. The doctor tells her that there are many curves. When talking to the doctor, Mrs. den Hartog seems to relax a bit. She watches the monitor. After a few minutes, the doctor says: "We are going back now. I saw a small polyp on the way up. I will look for it on the way back."

A few instants later, the endoscope stops moving. "*Yes, here it is,*" Mrs. den Hartog says. She has never seen a polyp before, yet she recognizes the bulge in the intestinal lining shown on the monitor. It must be a polyp, since it looks different from its surroundings and the doctor said that she saw a polyp. "Yes, there is one here", the doctor confirms, "but there is also one more a bit further down". "*How big is a polyp anyway?*", Mrs. den Hartog wants to know. "*What should I imagine?*" "Small, very small", the doctor replies. "*Not like a pinhead, is it?*", Mrs. den Hartog wonders. "Usually they are about two to three millimeters." "*Really? It looks much bigger.*" The nurse gives the endoscopist a small biopsy forceps, which she inserts into one of the channels inside the endoscope. On the monitor, a pair of cutters appears. Mrs. den Hartog does not look at the monitor. On the doctor's command, the nurse 'takes a small bite'[55] from the polyp and pulls back the forceps. She drops the small piece of tissue in a jar, which is marked and set aside.

The doctor continues. Mrs. den Hartog closes her eyes every now and then, sighs and moans softly. She needs all her attention to cope with the pain caused by cramps inside. "You can pass some gas", the nurse says. "*I try to, but I am not used to that. A lot is between the ears you know.*" Mrs. den Hartog has learned that it is impolite to fart in the company of others.

After about 15 minutes, the examination is over. Four polyps have been found, in three different areas of the sigmoid. Two were burnt away, the others were sampled. While Mrs. den Hartog gets dressed, the physician tells her that irrespective of the lab results of the sampled tissue, it is very unlikely that her symptoms have been caused by the polyps. The polyps are too small too cause pain and they do not look actively malignant. There was no indication for any other cause either. Since polyps further up the colon could cause the kind of pain Mrs. den Hartog suffers from, the radiologist proposes to schedule an examination of the entire large intestine, a colonoscopy.

Ten weeks after the sigmoidoscopy, Mrs. den Hartog is back on the same examination table. Since she will undergo a colonoscopy this time she receives a sedative administered by drip during the examination.[56] A monitor shows her pulse and blood pressure, which is measured by a clip on one of her fingers. Although the medication makes her sleepy, Mrs. den Hartog sometimes watches the monitor and talks to the nurse, who encourages her to pass gas in case of cramps. This time, however, Mrs. den Hartog is not bothered by any cramps.

Occasionally, the monitor shows some yellow spots: excrements, the doctor explains. Mrs. den Hartog remarks that it is dirty, compared to what she saw ten weeks ago. She is unpleasantly surprised that her intestines are not clean after she drank three liters of laxative. The doctor explains that it is normal; regardless of the preparations, some fluid stools from

---

[55] Literal translation of the Dutch 'een hapje nemen'. The expression is used in physicians' and nurses' communication with patients, as well as among themselves.

[56] Because a colonoscopy takes longer than a sigmoidoscopy and enters further into the intestine, it is more likely that the pain caused by the examination interferes with the aim of a successful examination. The main effect of the medication is the relaxation of patients' muscles and bowels, making the examination easier for them as well as for the physician. In many countries, sedation is standard for colonoscopies. In the department where I did my observations, all gastroenterologists and some of the surgeons perform colonoscopies with sedation. Sigmoidoscopies are usually done without, unless the patient explicitly requested it, or was known as having had serious problems during a previous examination. Other surgeons prefer the patient to be as conscious as possible, in order for them to comply during the performance of interventions, like biopsies.

the small intestine enter the colon, but they can easily be sucked or flushed away through the endoscope. However, Mrs. den Hartog feels responsible and embarrassed. She repeatedly mentions how well she prepared for the examination, keeping the diet and taking the laxatives.

When the doctor announces she is nearing the end, Mrs. den Hartog asks how many centimeters she is in. "A meter now," the doctor replies. She asks Mrs. den Hartog to turn back to her left side. "We are almost there....... There we are!," the doctor says. Mrs. den Hartog: "*That is the stomach, isn't it?*" She thinks what she sees on the monitor now, is her stomach. It is not, however. In fact, it would be impossible to reach the stomach with an endoscope. The doctor links Mrs. den Hartog's remark not to what she sees but to what she must feel: "Do you feel this in your stomach? That is possible, the colon partly goes across the front of the stomach. Or actually, it goes behind it, I should say. We are at the beginning of the colon now. Now we go back and I spray it clean a bit."

In order to make sure she has seen the entire colon, the doctor asks Mrs. den Hartog to turn on her back again. Responding to Mrs. den Hartog's question whether she saw anything odd, she says she did not. The endoscopy has not identified any tangible cause of abdominal pain which would justify a diagnosis or treatment. "*So the pain has been caused by something like a spastic colon then?*" Mrs. den Hartog asks. "That might be. It cannot be the polyps. They are too small. A polyp can only cause pain when it obstructs part of the bowel. But not in this case. We will take another look in six years."

Momentary compositions

The real-time imaging technologies that were used to examine Mr. Coenen, Mrs. Vermeulen, Mrs. den Hartog and the other patients whom I observed in the hospital, produce momentary images. Doctors as well as patients can watch images of bodily interiors while they are being made, and only then, since the images vanish immediately, except for some prints or stored stills. The monitor provides a 'live' view inside a body. Real-time imaging leaves few material traces. In ultrasound and fluoroscopic examinations, a limited number of prints and digital stills are saved for future reference. Most endoscopic examinations do not produce any visual 'immutable mobiles'.[57] The majority of ultrasound, fluoroscopic and endoscopic

---

[57] Bruno Latour has introduced this term to describe two-dimensional, compact, stable and transferable pictures that can be easily compared to other data (cf. Latour 1990: 22).

images exist only temporarily, at a particular moment and in a particular place. They are composites of heterogeneous elements, including the hardware and software of a technological imaging device; a doctor and a patient, each with her or his own particular behavior; sensory perceptions; request forms and protocols; physical body parts; and a particular time-frame. What real-time images show, results from a specific configuration of elements at a particular point in space and time.

Although the ability to watch images is distributed among a variety of human and non-human actors involved in the production of connected body-networks and image-networks, visual perception is usually attributed to a singular entity: a doctor, a patient, a machine. Moreover, there is no doubt about the images' referent: during an examination, neither the physician nor the patient questions whether the pictures on the monitor represent the body on the examination table. However, a lot of work by physicians as well as by patients and machines is required in order to establish that relation. That work already starts before the examination, as described in the previous chapter. The 'body on the examination table' in itself is many things. For the physician, it is an imaging instrument and an object of visualization. For the patient, it is the object of examination and at the same time it is both source and object of visual and sensory perception.

During an examination, yet another body appears: the body on the monitor. The simultaneous presence of patients' bodies in various modes triggered the central question for this inquiry: what happens to embodied experiences of health or illness when one is able to have a real-time look into one's own interior? How do various modes of embodiment interact and affect one another? During imaging *events*, various modes of embodiment are enacted: the body a patient sees, feels and acts with; the body on the examination table that is the ultimate object of medical examination; and the body on the monitor as black and white shapes or colorful structures. A real-time imaging event present different modes of embodiment at the same time. After the event, bodies and images are disconnected. They get reconnected in various expressions of experience, as will be discussed in the next chapter. However, the real-time connection of bodies and images is actively being produced as well.

Image-body attachments

Medical imaging technologies mediate doctors' perceptions of patients' bodies as well as patients' perceptions of their own bodies and their conditions. Turning patients into potential spectators of their own interior bodies, real-time imaging technologies transform patients' perceptions and present their bodies in ways that differ from everyday experience.[58] The here-body on the examination table watches the monitor, listens to the doctor and feels the movement of the imaging device either on the inside or on the outside. The image-body on the monitor presents the patient's body as an object of visualization and observation, coinciding with but also different from the embodied spectator.

Sometimes an imaging event fails to construct a correspondence between the visual representations of a patient's interior and the supposed referent of those representations. In some cases the physician fails to establish a diagnosis and attributes this failure to a flawed imaging device or to the physical resistance of the patient's body. It may also be the patient whose physical sensations are at odds with what the monitor shows. The colonoscopy of Mrs. den Hartog provides an example of the latter. During the second inspection of her colon, Mrs. den Hartog linked what she saw on the monitor to what she felt inside her body. She thought she saw her stomach. The radiologist dismissed that conjecture and made a distinction between seeing and feeling.[59] Thus the radiologist presented herself as an expert in seeing and the patient as an expert in feeling: Mrs. den Hartog does not know what the radiologist sees, the radiologist does not know what Mrs. den Hartog feels. The separation of seeing and feeling and the privilege of the first over the latter is a feature of the entire set-up of real-time imaging rather than an individual action of the radiologist. It enacts an agential cut (cf. Barad 1996: 171). The radiologist grants herself with the agency to see and thus to obtain objective knowledge. The radiologist grants the patient her subjective experience, i.e. the agency to feel.

During a clinical examination physicians and patients alike tend to privilege medical expertise over embodied expertise.[60] Yet the story of Mrs. Vermeulen's agency in the

---

[58] Other medical images, like CT, MRI or PET scans, sometimes meet the eyes of the patient as well, and can become a powerful force in various public socio-cultural arenas (cf. Dumit 2004), but only after being processed and translated by experts in producing, interpreting and representing them.

[59] The actual expression that "there is a difference between seeing pain and feeling pain" comes from another imaging event I observed. During an endoscopy, the patient attributed the pain that he felt to a recent operation. The examination, however, did not indicate any such cause.

[60] See for instance Jose van Dijck's description of her own illness experience, in the Introduction to The Transparent Body (2005). Despite sharp pain attacks and continuous nausea for several weeks, she began to

production of fluoroscopic pictures of her bladder provides a counter-example. It showed that a doctor may need to know what a patient feels in order to understand what medical images are showing. In that case the doctor needed both the images and the patient's verbal expressions to 'see' whether or not something was wrong.. The distinction between knowledge as 'what doctors see' and experience as 'what patients feel' is not an intrinsic property of real-time medical imaging devices or events.

The stories of Mrs. Vermeulen and Mrs. den Hartog illustrate two ways in which patients' bodies are connected to images during real-time imaging events. The stories indicate that attachments like this can take various shapes. As an object of examination, a visualization instrument or as a spectator, a body can comply with or resist an imaging procedure. A patient can watch the monitor during the examination, yet she may also refuse to watch. Patients may recognize their own body on screen or think of what they see as pictures of an unknown world. Sometimes doctors and patients have lively conversations, other examinations take place in silence.

Despite the evanescence of the event and the images, real-time imaging is conditional upon the constitution of links between bodies and images. These attachments may last longer than the imaging event itself. Four modes of attachment can be identified, which are interlinked and may occur simultaneously during an examination: the real-time interpretation of images by medical professionals; patients' visual perceptions of images of their own interior body and simultaneous sensory perceptions of the imaging procedure; patients' physical agency during imaging; and patients' emotional responses to the images and the imaging procedure.

Real-time readings

Since the majority of images produced during real-time imaging events only make a one-time appearance, the interpretation of the images is mainly a real-time affair. A radiologist or a physician who performs an endoscopy has to decide during the examination which images potentially provide relevant data, for an immediate diagnosis, for future reference or to plan an intervention. Physicians' processing of pictures starts during the examination; they adjust contrast and colors, change angles, and add numbers, marks and words, thus translating

---

doubt her symptoms when both a gastroscopy and an ultrasound did not show any possible cause. When a blood-test showed that something was seriously wrong, she underwent emergency surgery.

pictures into data. They constantly go back and forth: between monitor and body, request and image, pictures and words, shapes and numbers. The patient is the physician's witness; Mr. Coenen, for example, attentively observed how the radiologist zoomed in, made marks, performed measurements and added text and numbers to the pictures.

Medical imagers are paradoxically iconoclastic, especially when they compare themselves to patients. When introducing myself and my research topic – simply put as 'the impact of real-time imaging on patients – several radiologists mentioned their surprise about what they considered patients' high expectations of imaging. "Patients always think we can see everything," a radiology resident said, "whereas, actually, only in about 30 % of the examinations we are able to see something." The radiologist did not mean to say that the other 70 % of the patients were okay. In many cases, imaging technologies were just not able to visualize the cause of a complaint. And in response to a patient who during an ultrasound examination remarked that the liver looked quite large, another radiologist stated: "You think it is large? You can have it any size you want," while he zoomed in and out, thus completely altering the image on the monitor. To professional imagers, imaging is about producing data, that can be represented visually, numerically or otherwise (Beaulieu 2002, cf. also Dumit 2004, Prasad 2005). Many radiological techniques actually involve the translation of audio (ultrasound) or numerical (MRI) into visual data, "as an afterthought that is markedly lacking in any aspect of visuality" (Sturken and Cartwright 2001: 300). Physicians need pictures in order to localize, estimate, measure and intervene, as instruments or data sources rather than as results or data. They regard images as objects to *read* rather than as objects to *see*.

During an examination, physicians address a patient's body as an object of investigation, which must be disclosed in order to show its possible deficiencies. Imaging technologies do not simply render bodies transparent, nor do they make disease or health visible. For physicians, images are semi-finished data sets that need to be transformed into data. It is from this perspective that a doctor points out to a patient what the monitor shows. To Mr. Coenen's question whether his left kidney looks worse than the right, for example, the radiologist replied: "Hard to say, it is difficult to quantify." Patients may feel that the relation between doctor and imaging technology is one of embodiment, whereby the monitor serves as a window to the patient's interior body. For doctors, however, their relation to the images and the imaging device is a hermeneutic one: they mark, measure and count, rather than merely look.

Although real-time images can be translated into two-dimensional, compact, stable and transferable pictures that may be easily compared to other data (cf. Latour 1990: 26), even prints, recordings and stored digital visual results of real-time imaging events never obtain the objective status of other visual medical data like X-rays or MRI-scans. The products of real-time imaging are unable to speak for themselves to physicians who have not been involved in their production. When the results of real-time imaging are communicated to the physician who requested the examination, the report usually consists of words and numbers and does not include visual data. Although pictures can be transferred to other physicians, they rarely are. A radiologist explained to me:

> It makes little sense to send prints of ultrasound images to the requesting doctor. You know, you can compare those stills to a frozen video image, they are just as hazy. Moreover, the saved images are only an anthology from the moving pictures. We have noticed that pictures do not add much to the report, as they are hardly looked at. Clinicians usually cannot do much with ultrasound stills, contrary to CT- and MRI-scans. Those are objective images, which clinicians themselves can interpret as well.

Yet while pictures of real-time imaging events are harder to read than quantitative data, they are still more tangible than the patients' bodies themselves. Doctors can do things with images they cannot do with bodies: save them, edit them and compare them. That gain, however, implies a considerable loss. Whereas real-time imaging for doctors involves feeling the imaging device and listening to the patient, such additional 'live' information is lost outside the examination room. That is even true for the video recordings made of particular fluoroscopic and endoscopic examinations.[61] Even moving pictures of a full examination are not a mere copy of a real-time imaging event, but a translation. The images are detached from the bodies they supposedly refer to. One can take time to read the pictures, rewind them, freeze them and rerun them. Their value may be compared to a recorded live television broadcast: the recorded images mean something different from the live ones, since it is exactly the simultaneity of the event and the image transmission that gives live television its particular impact. Nevertheless, recorded images contain traces of the actual event.

Images do not *show* health or disease. What they can show is abnormality compared to normal images: whether a lump is solid or filled with liquid or whether tissue is red or pink. A similar image in two different patients can come to refer to different 'causes'. What is the start

---

[61] A video recorder is a standard feature of endoscopy and fluoroscopy machines. Endoscopic examinations are rarely recorded, except for educational purposes or on special request, e.g. of an attending doctor who has not been able to perform the examination him- or herself. For some fluoroscopic examinations video recording is standard, like in defaecographies (recording the movements while a patient discharges contrast fluid from the bowels) and HSG exams (scouring the Fallopian tubes with contrast liquid).

of an infection in one person can be improvement or stabilization of the condition of another patient. What counts as health or disease is not simply decided on the basis of pictures. It is only in the pathology lab where an irregularity spotted through the endoscope turns out to be a malignant polyp.

The presence of the actual object of imaging – the patient's body – during the examination, as well as the conscious attendance of the patient, gives a real-time imaging event its distinct character when compared with other examinations like MRI- and CT-scans or X-ray. Most discussions about non-real-time medical images, take place in radiological *reading* and *conference* rooms. Although patients sometimes get to see some of the pictures after an examination or during a follow-up consultation, doctors are commonly the only ones to see medical images. A radiologist who translates X-rays or CT-scans into reports has usually not been involved in the hands-on production of the images, nor has she or he seen the actual patient. [62] In the reading room radiologists retrieve and interpret printed or digital pictures produced during various procedures and dictate the reports of those examinations. In a conference room, radiologists, assistants, students and physicians from other departments discuss a selection of pictures that are particularly interesting for educational or broader diagnostic purposes. In the case of real-time imaging, the examination room functions as production room, reading room and conference room all in one.

For non-real-time images, professional intersubjectivity, institutionalized in reading and conference rooms, translates initial deliberations into the most objective findings possible. Real-time imaging requires a different routine. Although real-time reading follows similar routes and protocols, those remain inaccessible to other physicians. The few pictures that continue to have some kind of material presence – either in print or digital – are relatively insignificant as results of a real-time imaging event. They rather serve as reminders, or anchors for the reading of images that have ceased to exist materially.

Real-time imaging allows for constant feedback between monitor, physician, nurse and patient. Patients like Mr. Coenen and Mrs. den Hartog ask the doctor what he or she sees, what the doctor is looking at or whether a particular image is normal. They thus evoke the expression of a particular reading, which may include elements that may not directly follow from, or be that relevant to, the reason why the examination has been requested. During an abdominal ultrasound examination I recorded the following conversation between a

---

[62] Image acquisition is the job of radiology assistants or technicians.

radiologist and a patient, who had just explained that one of her kidneys had been surgically removed:

R	And where is your gallbladder? Gone as well?
P	Yes, ha-ha, you could search for that for a long time!
R	Could you please tell me what else you are missing?
P	My appendix, parts of my pancreas.
R	This happened to me before this week, that I was looking for over a minute to find the uterus, and then the lady told me it had been removed!

In this example, the radiologist benefited from the patient's presence in the interpretation of the images on the monitor. The eventual report, however, usually does not contain such information. Characteristic for real-time imaging is that research data (real-time images) only exist during an examination, where they are connected – both materially and in time – with their eventual referent (the patient's body). Physicians filter those qualities from the data as much as possible by storing only still pictures and their translations into numbers and words. The evanescence of the images and the presence of the patient, however, inform patients about the process of knowledge production.

Some physicians extensively inform patients about what they do and see during an examination. Intentionally or unintentionally, doctors communicate 'results' to patients during or immediately upon the examination, although they themselves do not consider them as results yet. Sometimes physicians explicitly reflect upon the limited value of an examination. I observed radiologists stating to a patient after an ultrasound that "the kidneys look ok, but that does not tell you anything about how they function" or that "the liver looks a bit fatty, but that can indicate many things".

Patients usually hear the final results of a real-time imaging event from a physician who has not seen the images. The final results are communicated several days or weeks after the examination, yet patients are often told some preliminary results – something like "the ultrasound does not show anything special" – during or immediately after the examination from the performing physician. They have witnessed a crucial phase in the interpretation of the images, but there is no actual diagnosis yet. The results of real-time imaging that patients eventually obtain, do not carry any material trace of the imaging event. Yet they do refer to that event somehow. In the next chapter I will argue that both the results and patients' own memories of the examination are sources that may contribute to the enactment of patients' illness experience.

Doctors' real-time readings inform patients' perceptions of their own body. The endoscopic pictures of Mrs. den Hartog's intestine, for instance, showed polyps – something obvious to the doctor, who, has learned through training and experience what normal colons and polyps look like. Mrs. den Hartog saw polyps as well, for the first time in her life. When the doctor pointed out what a polyp looked like, Mrs. den Hartog started to look for them. She assessed anything she saw: is it normal, and if not, could it be a polyp? Thus during the examination, Mrs. den Hartog acquired potential visual referents for her physical inconveniences, as well as a new way to perceive her own body.

The quantity and quality of verbal and non-verbal communication between doctors and patients during examinations diverged significantly. Sometimes, doctors actively involve patients in the production of images and in watching them. Some physicians explicitly point to the possibility of watching the monitor during an examination. Yet during the examination, they may not explain anything about what is shown. Others give an almost streaming commentary.[63] Patient's presence during the interpretation of real-time images affects how doctors talk about images. Besides a biomedical vocabulary doctors use another language to talk about images in real-time imaging events, which is used to address the patient. It consists of every-day language, featuring elements from what could be called a psycho-social vocabulary. In endoscopic events, this is usually the main vocabulary of the nurse during an examination.

Language does not merely express visual observations, but transforms the object of real-time imaging , since "by the use of a certain vocabulary, a reality is created in which people, things, facts, values and acts get allotted their own place and meaning" (Mesman 2002: 43, translation MR). That is why an analysis of doctor-patient communication in real-time imaging events is crucial to understand technological mediations of embodied experience. In their interactions with doctors, instruments, nurses and images, patients obtain a particular 'endoscopic' gaze (cf. Van Dijck 2001) that informs their embodied experience.[64] Doctors and patients delegate part of their search for diagnosis and treatment to imaging devices. The collective work of doctors, machines and bodies in real-time imaging gives patients the impression that doctors can see what is wrong with them.[65]

---

[63] Not only a patient might require or invite a more or less detailed commentary by the doctor, my presence as a researcher might have done that as well. Some doctors and nurses told me that some doctors tended to explain patients more, since they knew I was interested in how patients experienced examinations.

[64] 'Endoscopic' not in the medical, but in the literal sense of 'a view within', derived from the Greek *endo* (within), and *skopein* (to view).

[65] This argument will be further developed in chapter 5.

It is not my primary aim to describe technological mediations of medical professionals' agency and experience.[66] However, during real-time imaging, knowledge production, agency and perception are distributed among physicians, patients and imaging technologies. An account of patients' mediated embodied experience – which *is* my primary aim – therefore must include the work of medical professionals. Patients' presence during physicians' real-time readings of medical images – i.e. the translation of patients' bodies into discursive objects via images – transforms patients' perceptions of their body as it lies on the examination table and appears on the monitor. The same goes for the technical and professional preparations described in the previous chapter and for the diagnostic work discussed in the next chapter.

Seeing one's own interior

The possibility for patients to watch the imaging being produced in real-time constitutes another mode of attachment. Apart from for example fluoroscopic examinations of the colon, which require positions and physical activities from patients that do not allow them to watch the monitor, the set-up of most other examinations I observed enabled patients to watch the monitor at least during part of the examination. Indeed, the sight of the monitor was hard to avoid in examination rooms, since it is the main source of light in a scarcely lit room and the main object of attention for the doctor. Often doctors invite patients to watch the monitor and 'see for themselves'. That is what Mr. Coenen did. He carefully screened the monitor during the examination, asked questions about what he saw and shared his own interpretations with the radiologist. However, I also observed patients who did not watch the monitor at all during the examination. One of them was Mr. Simons. During the ultrasound examination of his kidneys, he looked at the ceiling and the walls of the examination room and not once inquired about what the radiologist did or saw. He felt the transducer, heard the beeps, changed position, and regulated his breathing upon the doctor's request, but he did not look at the monitor. When I asked him after the examination why he had not watched the monitor, he replied: "I do not see anything anyway. Those people know more than I do."

Unlike Mr. Simons, Mr. Coenen and Mrs. den Hartog were fascinated by the images, even if they had no medical background either and were unfamiliar with the kind of images

---

[66] Several authors have done that thoroughly and eloquently among whom Blume (1992), Pasveer (1989) and Saunders (forthcoming).

that appeared on the monitor. Just like any other patient, they had received an information flyer that focused on the physical preparations required for their examination and on the possible inconveniences, but that contained no information about what the monitor would show and what that could tell them. Mr. Coenen and Mrs. den Hartog, however, expected the monitor to show something about themselves. Like many other patients, they did not recognize the images that appeared on the monitor, yet they had no doubt that what they were watching was their own body. While Mrs. den Hartog looked at the screen, she felt the endoscope inside her body and the cramps caused by the inflated air. When the doctor removed a polyp, Mrs. den Hartog averted her eyes, apparently not wishing to see this surgical intervention, although she later told me that she did not feel the sample being taken or the polyps being removed. In response to a question I posed to him after the endoscopic examination of his colon, Mr. Theunissen, who was introduced in chapter 2, remarked:

> MR   When you see those images, you know that: this is my body, this is me?
>
> MT   Yes. You feel that, you know? You feel that tube right here in your guts. You can feel approximately where they are with that tube.

During the production of images, fluoroscopy, ultrasound and endoscopy establish bodies as objects of patients' tactile perception to various degrees. A fluoroscopy machine sends and receives X-rays, without physically touching the body. The high-frequency sound signals emitted by an ultrasound transducer only reach their destination – and are bounced back – when the probe moves across the skin rubbed with gel. An endoscope literally enters the body; it temporally becomes part of it, touching the body on the inside. Since patients know that the images on the monitor are produced by a camera in the tube that they feel moving inside them, it must be their own body appearing on the screen. Pain and discomfort cause doctor and patient to constantly shift focus from body to monitor and vice versa.

Mr. Simons and other patients who do not watch the monitor during an examination, undo the simultaneous presence of their image-body as an object of visual exteroception and their proprioceptive here-body.[67] Mr. Simons did not establish a visual link between his own lived body and the real-time pictures on the screen, yet he created other links that enabled the production of usable images, actively complying to the doctor's breathing instructions. To the construction of a medical, diagnostic meaning for the examination, it is irrelevant whether or

---

[67] In psychology and phenomenology, the term exteroception is used to describe perception by means of the five senses open to the external world: sight, hearing, touch, taste and smell. Proprioception is the "unconscious" awareness of where the various regions of the body are located at any one time and includes balance, position, and muscular tension (Leder 1990: 39).

not a patient watches the monitor. It is significant, however, for my analysis of the enactment of embodied experiences of illness. The previous and present chapters constitute the first steps in that analysis, which will be completed in the next chapter. When a patient does not watch the monitor during an examination, a characteristic constituent of real-time medical imaging experience - i.e. the possibility to go back and forth between the body on the monitor and the body on the examination table provided by the collective set-up of the examination- largely disappears. By not watching the monitor, Mr. Simons perceptually separated his image-body from his here-body. His body was instrument and object of imaging, but not a spectator of the images. For Mr. Coenen, however, real-time images provided opportunities to perceive, act, communicate and understand. As a spectator, he experienced his body through the images, not merely as an object of medical investigation but as his own.

However, even when a patient does actually watch the monitor, it is not self-evident that the visible body on the screen refers to her or his own body. The simultaneity of seeing and feeling one's body that makes real-time imaging stand out from many other medical mediations of embodiment, does not automatically result in a patient's identification with the images on the monitor. The story of the fluoroscopic examination of Mrs. Vermeulen's urinary tract, for example, showed how the simultaneous presence of a growing black spot on the monitor and the sensations of an increasingly full bladder occurred simultaneously, yet the visual perception and the physical sensation emerged separately. Whereas for the radiologist the sight of a patient's bladder filled with contrast fluid evoked an almost physical sensation of urge, Mrs. Vermeulen endured the increasing pressure on her bladder for a long time. She saw her bladder growing bigger on the monitor, yet she lacked the visual literacy to interpret that perception as abnormal.

On the other hand, I have also observed patients who were able to predict what the images would show on the basis of physical sensations. Patients with chronic conditions often become experienced spectators. One of them was Mr. Theunissen. Suffering from a chronic bowel infection, he has experienced numerous endoscopic examinations. I observed the examination and afterwards asked him what he saw.

MT   You immediately saw those red and white spots, that is not okay. It was even worse than last time.

MR   Why was it worse?

MT   Well, you saw many of those white spots, those are infections. Actually, that is not good.

(...)

MR   What did you expect from this examination?

MT   In fact, it is always the same, you know. You feel it has just stayed the same.

MR   And that is also what the doctor said now?

MT   Yes, it is just a check-up, they want to have a look.

Medical inspection by means of visualization and by means of physical examination are often complementary. Successful real-time imaging requires and evokes visual as well as haptic involvement of doctors and patients. Real-time imaging produces both images patients can see and sensations they can feel. The real-time simultaneity of seeing and feeling may constitute an unique perceptual link between the images on the monitor and one's own body.

Sedatives interfere with this simultaneity of seeing and feeling one's own body. In endoscopic examinations the use of sedatives (a 'glow', or in Dutch a 'roesje') is fairly common. For most colonoscopies it is standard. For sigmoidoscopies it is not, because of the limited duration of the examination.[68] When a patient is sedated during an endoscopic examination, the link between feeling (pain) and seeing one's own interior body is partly discontinued. During her second endoscopy, Mrs. den Hartog received a sedative. Compared to the first examination, the association between her visual perceptions of the images on the monitor and the endoscope moving through her body appeared to be weaker. The medication often affects both patients' visceral perceptions and their ability to watch the monitor. The sedative makes them sleepy and they regularly doze off. Although Mrs. den Hartog largely stayed awake and was aware of what happened on the monitor and in the examination room, her body was affected rather differently by the second examination compared to the first one. During the second examination, Mrs. den Hartog was not seriously bothered by cramps or other physical discomfort. The relaxation of her muscles and bowels made the examination easier on her and gave the physician smoother access to her interior body. The sedatives made the simultaneous haptic and visual perception of her interior body less urgent. They also affected her ability to act.

---

[68] For some fluoroscopic examinations, patients also receive medication to relax their muscles and prevent bodily resistances. Ultrasound examinations do not require such interventions, since the procedure is largely painless, even if the pressure on a patient's body may hurt in some cases.

Active dispossession

A particular kind of 'ability to act' constitutes a third mode of attachment that may be constitutive for a patient's experience of illness. It is the agency to be passive. The stories of Mr. Coenen, Mrs. Vermeulen and Mrs. den Hartog have shown examples. All four examinations that were presented, called for the patient's active participation in submitting her or his body to the imaging apparatus, which required more or less physical effort. Despite sometimes unpleasant sensations, the three patients attempted to relax, breathe on command and move when required. Like most patients, they were cooperative, because they considered their examination to be a prerequisite for diagnosis and possible treatment, resulting in the recovery or improvement of their abilities to cope with everyday life.

The success of real-time imaging depends on a delicate balance between patient's passivity and activity. Patients' cooperation and compliance are necessary conditions for successful imaging (cf. Burri 2001: 280). Real-time examinations may fail to result in diagnostically or therapeutically useful medical data. Even when a patient intends to subject her or his body to medical inspection, the body may not comply with real-time imaging requirements. Bowels can still contain excrements despite the patient's intake of prescribed laxatives, as in the case of Mrs. den Hartog. A curve in the large intestine can prevent the progress of an endoscopy. Sometimes contrast fluid is not distributed evenly during a colon fluoroscopy. And when a patient has been not been able to drink enough water and hold it, it is impossible to produce a meaningful ultrasound image of the maximum contents of a bladder. The body has a material agency to resist the process of collective embodiment and equipment of a body fit-for-imaging that I described in the previous chapter.

The responsibility for a body's compliance is distributed among patient, imaging machine, and doctor. In the first endoscopic examination of Mrs. den Hartog, the endoscopy was able to pass a curve in the bowel. By pushing on Mrs. den Hartog's abdomen, the nurse attempted to make her body comply. In addition, the doctor asked Mrs. den Hartog to move in order to manipulate her unwilling body. In the case of Mrs. Vermeulen, the radiologist was fully dependent on not only her body's compliance, but on Mrs. Vermeulen's verbal and embodied expressions of her physical experiences as well.

Actively attaching their bodies to the imaging apparatus, patients share in a collective, distributed agency. In the present and in the previous chapter, I have identified the "techniques, settings, devices and collective carriers which make this active dis-possession possible" (Gomart & Hennion 1999: 221). Bruno Latour has called it *actantiality*: "what *provides* actants with their actions, with their subjectivity, with their intentionality, with their morality" (Latour 1999b: 18).

Real-time images would not exist without patients' cooperation and compliance. The simultaneous active and passive involvement of patients' bodies in image production is visualized and materialized by the pictures on the monitor. It informs patients' embodied experience. For their part, images provide patients with the possibility of spectatorship, another form of active engagement.

Moved by pictures

Besides visual and sensory perceptions, emotions are a way in which patients are attached to real-time images and to the imaging procedure. When the inability of images to present a readable body is ascribed to a non-compliant body, patients sometimes get angry, disappointed, or embarrassed, like Mrs. den Hartog when she discovered that her colon was not entirely free from excrements despite her laborious purging. Although both the nurse and the physician told her that this was not uncommon and that it could be solved by technological means, i.e. by flushing water through the endoscope, Mrs. den Hartog felt responsible and somewhat guilty.

The story of Mrs. den Hartog exemplifies another mode of patients' affective attachment to images as well. During her first endoscopy, Mrs. den Hartog suffered from painful cramps, caused by the air inserted into her colon to provide the physician visual access. The nurse encouraged Mrs. den Hartog to relieve the discomfort and break wind. She assured her that this was an entirely normal thing to do in this situation and nothing to be embarrassed about. Since it would only be the clean inflated air that would be relieved, it would not even smell. Yet Mrs. den Hartog could not do it. Even in this extraordinary situation she could not give up the idea that breaking wind in the company of others is indecent. Although in theory Mrs. den Hartog did have the agency to relieve some of the discomfort that the examination caused her, her embarrassment prevented her to do so in practice. A similar emotion arose when the doctor identified the yellow spots that appeared on the monitor as excrements. At first, the monitor showed images that Mrs. den Hartog felt that she was physically connected to, yet did not represent her body as a recognizable part of herself. Then the doctor translated the images into a recognizable feature of one's body –

something one usually prefers to keep for oneself, so intimate that is a cause of embarrassment when seen by others.

A very common emotion for patients in real-time imaging events is fear. For many patients, the period before an examination is one of uncertainty. They worry about complaints they have sometimes been experiencing for a long time already or about symptoms which have deteriorated over a period of time. The examination might show that something serious is wrong. Several patients regard the images on the monitor with mixed feelings: awe and fascination on the one hand, fear and avoidance on the other. Sometimes an examination arouses sadness and feelings of loss, evoking old sores, reminders of past illnesses and medical treatments. Patients affective attachment to images and imaging has "to do with entering into a world of strong sensations; of accepting that 'external' factors take possession of the self; of being 'under the influence' of something else; of bracketing away one's own control and will in order to be expelled or rendered 'beside oneself' "(Gomart & Hennion 1999: 221). When emotions come into play, it becomes apparent that imaging does not merely affect one's body, but oneself.

Images of bodies

In the preceding paragraphs I have identified four ways in which patients' bodies are attached to images over the course of real-time imaging events. First, bodies and images are connected in physician's real-time readings of the images and in the communication between doctors and patients during an examination. In the second mode of attachment, the simultaneous visual and haptic involvement of patients in the production and watching of the images contributes to the possibility of patients to identify with the images on the monitor. Third, imaging makes patients participate in a network of distributed agency, being active and passive at the same time. And finally, patients may get emotionally attached to imaging and images.

One way of reading these modes would be to consider the first as a mode of patients' bodies' *objectivation*, and the others as modes of *subjectivation*. In those terms, the last three modes of attachments (sensory, agential and emotional) constitute links between subjects and their objectified bodies that result from the first mode of attachment (professional real-time reading). However, the fact that these modes of attachments occur in real-time and often simultaneously, renders distinctions between body-objects and embodied subjects, which may seem clear-cut in other practices of (medical) representation, problematic. What happens when image, reading, perception, agency and feeling are joined in space and time and collectively come to form the referent for a stream of real-time images? How does real-time imaging inform or transform people's notions and experiences of selves? What happens to the relation between represented and experienced bodies in real-time imaging events, and to the relation between image-body and here-body, that phenomenologists continue to distinguish despite their relational, constructivist notions of experience? And what about the anthropological distinction between disease and illness?

Understanding experience in terms of attachment opens up paths to address those questions. In networks that consist of discursive, visual, haptic, agential and affective links between bodies and images, real-time images can become 'subjectifiers' (Latour 2005: 212): representations of patients' *own* bodies. A description of real-time imaging as an event shows "how artifacts actively co-shape the events around them, and to understand these events not only in terms of *action* but in terms of *experience* as well" (Verbeek 2005b: 134, emphasis in original).

Real-time medical imaging interferes with patients' perceptions as well as with their physical bodies, thus offering particular possibilities for the images to re-present one's body, oneself and/or one's illness. The establishment and maintenance of material, discursive, agential, perceptual and emotional links between body and image can create a synecdochal relation between the objectified patient body on the monitor and the lived body on the table (cf. Cussins 1998). Synecdoche – images that come to stand for an embodied condition – is not a self-evident outcome of a real-time imaging event, however. A patient may feel pain, even if the doctor cannot see any cause for it. In examinations carried out for screening purposes, something may be found while the potential 'patient' feels fine. When visual and tactile perceptions of one's body do not match, or even contradict, one's own body is not a consistent referent of the produced pictures. The extent to which patient bodies get attached to an imaging apparatus, and the degree of correspondence between embodied spectator and corporeal spectacle, vary. Such different experiences of real-time imaging may reflect what I have called agential cuts. Various modes of agency – perceiving, knowing, feeling, experiencing - are distributed in an imaging event-network, yet both doctors and patients mistakenly attribute them to a singular actor, whether a body, a patient, a doctor or a technological device.

Like any other technology, real-time imaging affects existential as well as hermeneutic relations between people and their bodies. Technologies transform people's embodied existence in the world, as well as their embodied perception of the world, including their own bodies. However, the particularities of real-time imaging – the evanescence of the produced images and the real-time attachment between image-body and here-body – require an analytical frame geared to its specific nature.

Productions of presence

In the previous chapter I have used an actor-network approach to account for the enactment of patients' bodies as both potential objects and subjects of real-time imaging in various actors' preparations for imaging events. In the present chapter I have extended that approach to include the emergence of embodied subject positions in real-time imaging events. I have described which relations are established between bodies and images. However, to attain my ultimate goal – an understanding of technological mediations of embodied illness *experience* – I need to describe the specificities of real-time attachments of bodies to images: the ephemerality of the images and the simultaneity of seeing and feeling one's body. How do the black circles on the ultrasound images affect Mr. Coenen's understanding and experience of his illness? Does Mrs. Vermeulen have a different body now that the fluoroscopic examination showed she has an abnormally large bladder? Does Mrs. den Hartog still feel ill now that the endoscopies have not found any cause for her complaints? What do images do in relations between bodies, images and selves? In the next chapter, I will deal with these type of questions. To be able to do so, however, I need a more specific vocabulary to describe the attachments of bodies and images in real-time.

Many, but not all people have experienced real-time medical imaging, yet most people regularly watch real-time images of their own bodies in the mirror. In addition, many people have the experience of seeing live pictures of themselves on security monitors in department stores and supermarkets. When projected onto mirrors and screens, one sees oneself as if through the eyes of somebody else. Furthermore, a mirror undeniably shows an image of oneself.

Mirror-images serve as a subtext for patients' reading of real-time medical images. At first sight, the differences between mirror images and real-time medical images may be more striking than the similarities. A mirror shows the outside of the body, which is immediately recognizable as one's own body. By contrast, the interior body visualized in medical images does not resemble one's body as one knows it. A mirror image is indexical,[69] whereas a medical image is iconic and requires some knowledge about the depicted object and the technology of representation. Similar to a mirror,[70] however, a monitor showing real-time images transforms not only one's perception, but also one's agency, because it allows one to go back and forth between being a body and having a body (cf. Callon and Rabeharisoa n.d.).

The certainty of knowing a mirror to reflect oneself is not merely a matter of immediate recognition of one's outer appearance, but also has to do with the real-time nature of the mirror image. When standing in front of the mirror, we immediately see every move we make. The spectator of mirror images is not only subject of vision but also the producer of images. The simultaneity of acting and seeing one's actions and their affects establishes a direct link between the body in the mirror and the person in front of it. A mirror makes one's body present in a particular way. It is in this *production of presence* (Gumbrecht 2004) that mirror images and real-time medical images are comparable. The subtext of the mirror structures patients' attachments to real-time medical images.

An analysis of real-time medical imaging in terms of embodied experience involves the body as both subject and object of experience. Different modes of being and having a body, resulting from particular practices of embodiment, give rise to particular experiences of one's own body. Those experiences do not merely consist of ideas about what particular phenomena mean in relation to oneself, but they also entail the material, perceptual impact of those phenomena on one's body and senses. In a plea for an analysis of aesthetic experience beyond semiotics, literary scholar Hans-Ulrich Gumbrecht refers to that impact as 'presence' (Gumbrecht 2004). Gumbrecht argues that a description of (aesthetic) experience cannot be limited to the interpretation of meanings. An account of experience should address how objects are presented in such way that they initiate or intensify a tangible, immediate impact on human bodies and their senses (Gumbrecht 2004: xiii).[71] Such perspective is not an alternative to interpretative frameworks, but an indispensable supplement.

---

[69] An index is a physical sign or mark left by an object, e.g. a fingerprint. In the case of a mirror image, there is a direct physical link between the body in front of the mirror and the body reflected in it.

[70] Or rather, to 'a hall of mirrors', as Francisco Varela has described his experiences with medical imaging following a liver transplant (Varela 2001: 261).

[71] Mark Hansen has presented a similar idea in his *Embodying Technesis: Technology beyond writing (2000)*. In the introduction to that book, Katherine Hayles states that Hansen argues that "a highly sensitive and interactive realm of experience exists that precedes linguistic expression and legitimately counts as cognition (....) such experiences function as nonverbal avenues through which humans experience technology in its robust materiality. By attending to these "shocks", we can understand technology as an important experience in our lives beyond how it is represented in language" (Hayles in Hansen 2000: vii). What Hansen calls 'shocks', Gumbrecht calls 'productions of presence'.

The preceding analysis of technologically mediated embodiment and the distributions of agency it implies, has not sufficiently addressed the agency of one of the two protagonists in my argument: the images. It has mainly focused on (collective) patient bodies. The concept of presence describes the role of images in distributions of perceptual agency. Although technologically mediated experiences of health and illness hardly qualify as aesthetic, the concept of 'presence' is very relevant to my analysis of such experiences.

The idea of 'presence' as constitutive of experience resonates with the phenomenological concept of 'being-in-the-world' (Heidegger 1962). It is a relational quality, not an individual attribute. It characterizes human existence as physically and spatially immersed in its environment, which cannot be described in terms of distinct subjects and objects. Human beings exist in their interactions with the world. From a confrontation between this perspective and an ANT-approach (cf. Verbeek 2005a) it follows that 'the world' exists in interactions with human, non-human and hybrid. Beings exist in their ability to act, in their agency. The concept of 'presence' can describe perception as an analogous mode of being. Perception, as a particular category of action, constitutes observer and observed in relation to each other. 'Presence' is the result of such a relation. The modes of attachment I have described are such relations, as they constitute particular embodied presences. Like mirrors, real-time medical images constitute a direct perceptual link between body and image.

The limits to semiotic readings of experience become particularly problematic in the study of experiences of moving pictures (Gumbrecht 1998). The real-timeness of fluoroscopic, ultrasound and endoscopic pictures makes the need to address productions of presence as well as meaning particularly urgent, because the primary products of real-time imaging events materially vanish as soon as they have been made. The same is true for mirror images: they only exist as long as one stands in front of the mirror. The physical link gives mirror images their indexicality. Unlike other medical images, real-time medical images share these indexical qualities. They are icons, i.e. they need an informed reader to be medically meaningful, yet they are able to show non-informed spectators something about themselves by means of simultaneous visual, sensory, agential and emotional attachment.

Real-time imaging presents patients' bodies that have been prepared as hybrid collectives upon entering the examination room. Attached to imaging technologies, bodies are present in several modes at once. The evanescence of that simultaneous, distributed and hybrid presence gives real-time imaging its public aura of immediacy and transparency, an aura often at odds with professional notions and patients' perceptions of imaging in actual practice.

Real-time imaging is a particularly interesting case for challenging common distinctions between representations and experiences of one's own body, because it simultaneously mediates the visual experience of one's own body (when patients see the images) and one's sensory and emotional experience of the body (when patients feel the imaging device). Visual, sensory and emotional experiences are co-shaped in their mediation. The adagio "for every change in what is seen (…) there is a noticeable change in how (…) it is seen" (Ihde 1990: 79) is true for feeling as well. In real-time imaging, the seen and the felt, the seeing and the feeling body can not self-evidently be distinguished. What is more: a change in what is seen affects how it is felt, an alteration of what is felt affects how it is seen. By making parts of the interior body visible, real-time imaging transforms how that body is experienced.

The simultaneity of seeing, feeling and 'doing' one's body, however, does not imply that body and image coincide. Patients may identify with the images on the monitor, yet they are only indirectly affected. Phenomenologists have called the space between the body that perceives and the body that is perceived 'écart' (cf. Weiss 1999: 120; see also Varela 2001: 265). Technology enters that space and affects the lived body that is always both perceiver and perceived (cf. Ihde 2002: xi; Leder 1990: 63). By mediating between oneself as an embodied subject and one's body as an object, technologies offer patients particular possibilities to appropriate, or incorporate, material and perceptual features of their bodies that have been produced in their connections with others they would not be able to perceive otherwise. In the case of real-time imaging, those features include the visibility and spectatorship of one's own interior and one's sensory, active and emotional involvement in the production of the images.

From the analysis of processes of collective embodiment in the previous chapter and the collective productions of embodied *presence* in the present chapter, it becomes possible to address technological mediations of embodied *experience* in the next. The questions that I posed earlier in this section about how black circles affected Mr. Coenen's illness experience, whether Mrs. Vermeulen's body has changed and if Mrs. den Hartog still feels ill, are questions about experience rather than presence. Mr. Coenen's attentive spectatorship, Mrs. Vermeulen's active dispossession and Mrs. den Hartog's haptic and affective attachment constitute 'productions of presence' that condition technologically mediated experiences of illness.

Real-time presence and illness experience

After the notion of illness has been confronted with a composite, material body in the previous chapter, the present chapter has addressed the *techno-visual mediation* of embodiment. The use of actor-network theory to describe experience has resulted in an analysis that bears resemblance to the post-phenomenological approach introduced in chapter 2. Rather than the technological mediation of (illness) experience, however, the present chapter has described *conditions* for such experience: discursive, material, agential and emotional attachments of patients' bodies and real-time images. In medical anthropology, technology has commonly been described as widening the gap between 'disease' and 'illness'. With my analysis of attachments and productions of presence, I have shown how real-time imaging technologies mediate bodies that are 'objects' as well as 'subjects' of perception, knowledge and experience.

The anthropological distinction between illness and disease is a specific form of the subject/object separation that phenomenology attempts to overcome and that actor-network theory seeks to bypass. Describing productions of embodied presence renders both objectives feasible. I have presented professional real-time readings, patients' simultaneous visual and haptic perceptions, as well as their emotions and their bodies' material agency as alternative modes of attachment that cannot be understood independently. The construction of disease as a medical category and of illness as a mode of embodied experience converges in a real-time imaging event.

Anthropologists have studied illness experience through people's verbal, visual or behavioral expressions. Phenomenologists have complemented this approach with analyses of embodied perception. Yet, what has hardly been addressed in both anthropological and traditional phenomenological accounts of illness is the agency of materiality. An actor-network approach allows for an account of embodiment that includes the materialities of bodies and mediating technologies.

My analysis of the specific 'productions of presence' aligns a post-phenomenological frame with an actor-network account. The previous and the present chapter have provided a description of the equipment of patients' bodies as objects and subjects of medical visualization and of their attachment to images during real-time imaging events. Simultaneous presentations of bodies as objects of medical examination and as subjects of embodied perception enable the co-construction of what anthropologists have called disease and illness. What I prefer to call illness, to indicate that my ultimate object of analysis are patients' experiences, emerges in real-time imaging events as something one can see as well as feel, perceive as well as understand, and experience as well as know.

The four modes of attachment do not coincide with four categories of illness experience, but indicate various ways in which patients' bodies are produced in real-time imaging events. A body's presence is different when patients do or do not watch the monitor during an examination; when an instrument enters one's body or remains outside; when patients actively participate in the event, or when they do not. Various levels of physical activity and pain evoked by real-time imaging make patient bodies present in particular ways, since they relate patients' agency and the objectivation of their bodies. A more active involvement in that objectivation is more likely to constitute a perceptual link between oneself as an embodied actor and one's body as a medical object.

To obtain a durable referent, real-time images require translation. Two translation trajectories set off after an imaging event: one that aims at diagnoses and another that produces various expressions of experience. The first – the professional translation of imaging results into examination reports that contribute to a medical diagnosis – produces an 'objective' referent. The referent produced in the second trajectory is 'subjective': it is a patient's embodied experience mainly expressed in narratives. Those seemingly distinct referents, however, bear the marks of their joint origin that lies in the preparations of a body for real-time imaging – described in chapter 3 – and in the production of real-time images, described in the present chapter.

5   After the pictures: the embodiment of real-time medical images

When the pictures have vanished – except for a few stills or prints – and the patient has gone home, the next stage of real-time imaging sets in. The real-time connection of referent (body) and representation (real-time images) is broken after the examination. The present chapter inquires whether and how bodies and images get reconnected. 'Going after' the pictures, we follow translations of real-time image-body presences into embodied experiences of health and illness. Such translations actually take place at two distinct yet connected stages. First, medical professionals translate real-time imaging events into reports that may eventually contribute to a diagnosis. Second, patients translate real-time images into narratives that represent and construct their experience.

In chapter 2 I argued that neither medical anthropology nor (post-) phenomenology nor actor-network theory by itself affords a comprehensive analysis of technologically mediated illness experience in real-time imaging practices. In chapters 3 and 4 I showed why: an analysis of how bodies and images are presented requires insight in the configuration of a body-collective that precedes an examination. How real-time images affect patients' bodies depends on the networks in which they are acquired, shown, discussed and translated. Each configuration of actors inscribes images with a particular script that invites patients to have certain experiences (cf. Akrich 1992). Therefore I describe the entire network that enables images to affect the bodies of patients, including professional translations.

Physicians use stored pictures, words, numbers, other images and protocols to translate real-time imaging events into imaging reports. In the first part of this chapter, I describe their translation work and that of patients, as well as the connections between the various translations. For the larger part, patients express their experiences of imaging and embodiment narratively. They include and transform professional practices of reading and writing in their translations of imaging events. Professionals' and patients' translation trajectories cross ways and shape the other's direction. During consultation visits, physicians communicate examination results to patients. Consultations are the final destination of a medical-professional translation of real-time medical images into knowledge about disease.

Yet the patient's visit to the attending physician also presents a next stage in the translation of real-time medical images into patients' embodied identities and experiences of illness.

In the second part of this chapter, I describe how patients' and physicians' translations of real-time imaging events result in *image-bodies*, which – as objects of patients' experience – are part of patients' experiences of illness. Substituting the notion of 'mediation' by that of 'a body learning to be affected' makes it possible to describe the interconnected hermeneutic, material and existential interferences of real-time imaging with embodied illness.

Translation trajectories

Most of the images produced during a real-time imaging event disappear once the examination has passed. Yet real-time images do leave traces in the form of stills and prints, tissue samples, spoken and written words, numbers, reports and stories. Those are all translations of the real-time imaging event in which images and bodies are simultaneously produced. After the examination, the actors that collectively constituted an imaging network go separate ways. Their trajectories meet again during a follow-up visit to the doctor several days or weeks later, when an attending physician or general practitioner tells a patient the results of the examination and sometimes discusses a diagnosis or proposes a treatment plan.

In the meantime, doctors have discussed their findings, edited and stored stills, dictated reports and checked the written version. Assistants have sent tissue samples to the laboratory where they have been translated in more numbers and words. While a referent for the real-time images of their interior is being produced in the hospital, patients take their memories of the examination home with them: the sensations, the pictures, the doctor's explanations. Awaiting diagnosis, patients translate their experiences during real-time imaging events into mental images and into words and stories told to relatives, friends or an inquisitive anthropologist. Patients' experiences include their observations of professionals performing the examination. The results of the examination they eventually receive through their attending physician some days or weeks after the event, becomes part of patients' experience as well.

From images to reports

After she has pushed a button to stop the transmission of ultrasound signals, the radiologist puts back the transducer in its holder at the side of the monitor. She wipes the gel off Mr. Coenen's belly, says goodbye and leaves the examination room. In the central room of the ultrasound unit, right across the hallway, she walks straight to the dictation machine. She puts the request form, on which she has scribbled the sizes of the measured cysts and some other remarks during the examination, in front of her, turns on the recorder, and starts dictating: "Examination in preparation of kidney transplant, to check size of polycystic kidneys and presence of stones in gallbladder and urological tract. Both kidneys contain a pronounced quantity of cysts of various sizes...." Although the radiologist digitally stored several still images during the examination, she does not retrieve them. It takes the radiologist only a few minutes to finish dictating the report, during which she stops the recorder several times, to make corrections and rephrase remarks.

The recorded dictation is sent to the administration unit of the Radiology department. A clerk types it out and inserts it into the format for a radiological report. Order and phrasing are preserved for the most part, yet the clerk deletes some redundancies, and adds a few words to make a correct sentence. With another press of a button, the finished report is saved in the electronic patient file, where it can be retrieved by anyone who has access.

The next day, the performing radiologist – an assistant – finds the report in a pile of printed reports from other examinations she performed and which she has to check and sign. She quickly reads through it, finds no mistakes, and enters her initials. The report is sent back to the administration. A line is added to the digital report, stating that it has been confirmed, and including the names of the assistant and the supervising radiologists.

In the Internal Medicine Department, Mr. Coenen's attending physician retrieves the ultrasound report from the hospital network, along with the reports of the X-rays taken of the abdomen and of the jaw and teeth, which were performed right before the ultrasound. Including the chest X-ray performed two weeks earlier, none of the radiological examinations showed any contraindications for the start of dialysis and eventually a kidney transplant. Since an ECG and a duplex (ultrasound) examination of the blood vessels of the arm did neither, Mr. Coenen is 'diagnosed' as

fit for dialysis and transplantation. In due time, when his condition deteriorates,
dialysis will start. It may take years before transplantation, because kidneys are
scarce.

This is how the story of Mr. Coenen's ultrasonic kidneys (chapter 4) continued. Although the radiologist started reading in real-time, as I described in the previous chapter, image interpretation does not stop when image acquisition does. The moving pictures on the monitor in the examination room are ultimately translated into a diagnosis: an assessment of Mr. Coenen's fitness for dialysis. Although some still images are saved, the most sustainable result of imaging, which directs the further diagnostic and therapeutic trajectory of Mr. Coenen, is the written report. A physician who requested real-time imaging usually does not receive any pictures, but only a report by the physician who performed the examination. The images themselves are considered of little value for readers who have not been involved in their production. Since the only proper reader of real-time images is the person who produced them, other readers better confide in her or his informed reading. This is different for non-real-time pictures. X-rays, for example, are often sent to the requesting doctor right away, or physically taken there by the patient, to be followed only later by a radiologist's report. The attending physician may then compare his or her own reading to that of the specialized imager. The readings of real-time images by their producers usually lack such comparison.

In order to represent bodies according to medical standards of objectivity, real-time images require translation into non-visual data. X-rays, CT-scans or MRI-scans bring along their own context for interpretation. Conversely, the context required to read real-time images only exists during their production. Although all knowledge produced by means of imaging technologies is contextual, or situated (Haraway 1988), information needed to read still images is inscribed in the pictures themselves, rendering them 'immutable mobiles' (Latour 1990: 22), which can be read by professionals who have not been directly involved in their production. A still image can only be a read from a limited number of angles, whereas viewpoints are constantly being adjusted during real-time imaging. Real-time imaging reports represent evanescent images and owe their authority to their writers who have performed the search for the represented objects themselves. Written reports transform the simultaneous presence of professional reader, images and the object of visualization into an objective context supposed to compensate for the subjective status of real-time images among medical professionals.

It takes several stages of translation from images to report: from real-time pictures to verbal and written expressions made by the doctor during the examination, via a recording of a spoken interpretation and a transcribed report, to a juxtaposition of various images and reports and ultimately a therapeutic plan. To be diagnostically meaningful, real-time images usually need to be combined with other data sources. These can be produced in the context of an imaging event, such as tissue samples collected during an endoscopic examination, or they may result from other visual examinations or blood tests. Imaging results and other findings may be contradictory. An ultrasound, for example, may not show the presence of small gallstones that may nonetheless cause a patient a lot of pain reminding her of previous gall stone attacks. After a blood test indicates that something indeed is wrong, the gallstones can be visualized and removed during an endoscopic examination.[72] This example shows that a doctor might value a negative ultrasound over a patient's previous experiences and expressions of pain. A blood test, however, can overrule ultrasound results, after which endoscopy is used to verify and treat the problem. Images are thus weighed in relation to other findings. The decisive factor for a diagnosis can be the order of examinations, whether certain examinations and results are contested or not, or possibilities for treatment. From a variety of visual and other data, imaging physicians compose findings, which are further translated into diagnoses by attending physicians. Rather than representing a fixed body, pictures refer to other data and vice versa. A diagnosis represents a complex of referential chains.

The first translations of images, described in chapter 4, take place during the examination. Chapter 3 showed how the translation of bodies already starts before the examination. The material transformation of streaming images into stills or prints implies a change of meaning: the pictures are taken out of their context of production to be used in other settings. Endoscopy sessions usually leave few visual reminders of real-time imaging events. Prints are made only upon request of the referring physician, or to illustrate a diagnosis to patient or colleagues. Radiological examinations yield more 'immutable mobiles' in the form of stills, prints or video recordings.

During an ultrasound examination it is common practice to include at least one digital still of each examined organ. The visual record after an abdominal ultrasound, for example, usually contains at least one image of all major organs: liver, gallbladder and bile ducts, spleen, pancreas and aorta, and sometimes the kidneys. A radiologist may decide to freeze a

---

[72] Cf. Van Dijck 2005, ix-x.

picture because of particularly clear abnormalities considered illustrative for a specific condition (e.g. the large kidney cysts in the ultrasound examination of Mr Coenen) or, on the contrary, because of an unexpected situation (e.g. the cysts in Mr Coenen's liver found during the same examination) or one allowing multiple interpretations, even if it is neither immediately relevant to the presented question, nor cause for immediate clinical action .

Fluoroscopic examinations produce both digitally 'frozen' pictures and X-ray prints.[73] At set intervals stipulated in the examination protocol, the radiologist takes an X-ray picture of a particular situation, or asks the assistant to do so. For a micturating cysto-urogram (MCU), such as Mrs. Vermeulen's examination described in the previous chapter, six standard prints are made: before the catheter is entered, when the bladder is full, of the kidneys at this point, of the bladder and kidneys when urination starts, during urination, and of the bladder and kidneys after urination. These pictures are automatically sent to the printer and the prints are taken to the reading room to be examined by the radiologist later.

Apart from storage and editing, real-time images are translated into findings through *talking*. In the case of real-time imaging, the examination room functions as production room, reading room and conference room at once. Real-time images themselves do not appear in reading and conference rooms, and prints and digital stills produced during real-time imaging events do not frequently end up there, since their meaning is closely connected to the context of production. Despite several similarities between the verbal translation of real-time and non-real-time images, their role in the construction of medical findings is different.

Conversations about real-time images primarily occur in examination rooms during an examination. Real-time imaging escapes the routine of professional intersubjectivity symbolized by the radiological reading room: although real-time reading follows outlines and protocols similar to those for other examinations, its results remain inaccessible to other physicians. The few pictures that continue to have some kind of material presence – either in print or digital – are relatively insignificant as results of a real-time imaging event. They rather serve as reminders or anchors for the reading of images that have ceased to materially exist. Still pictures from real-time imaging event are only meaningful to those who were involved in their production, usually excluding other professionals than the examination's performer, yet including the patient.

---

[73] The kind of fluoroscopic examinations I observed were done for diagnostic rather than therapeutic purposes. Fluoroscopy is also used however to monitor/navigate surgical procedures (e.g. bone-setting, catheterization of blood vessels). Digital fluoroscopy offers even more possibilities. My remarks however only concern analogue, diagnostic fluoroscopic examinations of the digestive and urinary tract. The purpose of imaging is the production of images apt to be read afterwards, rather than of images instrumental to a surgical procedure or intervention.

Although I have attended examinations where few words were exchanged except for the customary courtesies between physician and patient, during most real-time imaging events physicians talk about what they see: to the assistant, to an attending colleague, to the patient and sometimes to his or her partner. Professional discussions about medical images, real-time or not, are often pursued largely along the lines of the request form and the anticipated report and feature language that is only comprehensible to insiders.

Most patients are not really familiar with the medical vocabulary used in discussions among medical professionals. For professionals, the shared language makes it possible to effectively communicate about images and share interpretations, ask for a second opinion or direct interventions. Some patients told me that the medical language, usually spoken in a low voice, obscures rather than clarifies what the monitor shows. However, patient's presence during the interpretation of real-time images affects how doctors talk about images. Besides biomedical language, doctors use every-day language to talk about images in real-time imaging events when they address the patient, like 'taking a bite' for a biopsy. The language used during an examination can thus be very different from the language used in a report. When an examination does not show any irregularities, radiologists as well as endoscopists often invite patients to watch the monitor to "see for yourself that everything is okay". Watching the monitor, however, does not provide patients with an actual diagnosis. For that and for the development of a treatment plan, patients are referred to their attending physician. When images have been selected, edited, stored, discussed, combined and compared, physicians translate them into reports. Below is the report that resulted from the radiological examination of Mr. Coenen. It only refers to particular parts of Mr. Coenen's body: his kidneys, liver, gallbladder, bile ducts, and bladder. It includes verbal and numerical, but no visual information. Pictures are translated into measurements and deviations from certain standards. What looks normal is only mentioned as background: standards and normal images act as an implicit frame of reference in the report.

Report ultrasound xx-xx-03

To   Outpatient department internal medicine

          <Name requesting doctor>

Ultrasound upper abdomen   Ultrasound kidney bs

Clinical information:

Preparation for kidney transplant. Size of polycystic kidneys. Stones in gallbladder or urinary tract.

Report:
In both kidneys a marked amount of cysts is present of different size. The largest on the right measures 7 ½ x 5 cm., the largest on the left 4,7 x 4,7 cm. Minimal remains of normal kidney tissues are discernible. As for size the kidneys fall out of transducer range, bs at least 18 cm., although as said, they fall out of range and are actually bigger. Identification of concretions inside those multiple cysts cannot be executed. In the liver at least about three cysts are observed, furthermore homogenous. Furthermore the gallbladder is slender, no concretions, no thickened wall. The ductus choledochus measures 6 mm., still within the norm. The bladder is fairly filled. No clear defects.

Conclusion:
Marked polycystic kidneys on both sides, both sides at least 18 cm. At least about three cysts in the liver. No cholelithiasis.

All imaging reports roughly follow a similar order that reflects the reading routine: first look at the question, then describe what you see, do measurements, compare to standards, and come to a conclusion. A report's conclusion presents findings as an answer to the question by the requesting physician, rather than a diagnosis. Different examinations have their own report formats, which leave room for various specialist and personal vocabularies. Endoscopy reports, for example, are more likely to include an account of the course of the examination than radiological reports, which reflect the different status of images in relation to other findings in endoscopic and radiological examinations. Furthermore, experienced imagers in radiology as well as in endoscopy often write more concise reports, including an overview of the situation according to the standards and the relevant abnormalities, and are more likely to mention a preliminary or possible diagnosis than less experienced colleagues. Residents, for whom it generally takes longer to perform an examination, often write longer reports as well, including their considerations to come to a certain conclusion. Thus imaging reports are selective accounts of imaging events rather than representations of bodies, body parts or medical conditions.

Real-time imaging reports read as if they have been written while the radiologist or endoscopist is watching the images. Except for fluoroscopy reports dictated in the radiological reading room while the radiologist is looking at the light box, however, doctors make reports without having the images at hand. Stored ultrasound pictures are consulted only in rare cases. A report based on stored images, however, is considered as less reliable than a report dictated immediately after an examination. A radiologist may need to postpone the writing of a report because of interfering duties, and may only be able to come back to it several hours or even days afterwards. In one such case, concerning a belated ultrasound report, the report stated that it was based on the 'assessment of pictures' and was therefore of limited value. This example shows how normally, real-time imaging reports refer to examinations rather than pictures of particular body parts. For a valid interpretation real-time reading is indispensable: pictures alone are not enough.

In the professional interpretation of real-time images, the pictures are largely stripped from the effects of realism that characterized their production: the real-timeness which makes it possible to watch pictures while they are made and the presence of the patient's body during image acquisition. When moving pictures produced during an examination are translated into reports, their referent is no longer the patient's body, but a data-set relative to standards. Medical images are not intended to resemble real bodies, but are topological constructs representing phenomena that cannot be fully understood from a singular perspective (cf. Saunders forthcoming).

Imaging reports represent data rather than bodies. To enable the translation of pictures into manageable bodies, reports present a fragmented body, translated into numbers and compared to certain standards. Yet the body presented in a report is also a whole, assembled from a variety of visual and non-visual data. Tissue samples, evaporated images, pictures, numbers and reports are brought together under the same heading: a patient with a particular name, sex, date of birth and patient number. Administrative structures, such as the practice to print or write the patient number on jars, reports and pictures, serve to guarantee that parts can stand for the whole. As *coordination tools*, reports connect the various referents of medical images: patients, body parts and medical conditions.

From reports to patients

After a quick yet extensive journey through the professional clinical imaging apparatus, translations of real-time imaging results ultimately return to patients. Reports of imaging events are stored in the hospital digital system, where they can be retrieved by patients' attending physicians who requested the examination. A printed copy is sent to applicants outside the hospital. The attending physician then communicates the results to the patient in a face-to-face consultation or on the phone. In most cases, doctors base their diagnosis and treatment on written verbal translations of real-time images without having seen any visual material themselves. The referent of the findings attending physicians communicate to patients are not images, but imagers' reports. Patients themselves usually do not receive a copy of the report.

The only pictures I saw being used in visits following real-time imaging events, were doctors' sketches made for patients to illustrate a finding or diagnosis, or anatomical illustrations available in the consultation room on which the physician points out the location of a particular finding. The actual visual products of the examination, the pictures, are entirely absent from consultations. What patients get there are not pictures, but their attending physician's verbal translations of other doctors' written reports.

Their real-timeness distinguishes ultrasound, fluoroscopy and endoscopy from many other diagnostic technologies. Unlike in other examinations, in real-time imaging events patients actually see the raw material on which doctors base their diagnosis. In the case of real-time imaging, doctor-patient communication is not limited to consultations about an examination's results between an attending physician and a patient several hours, days or weeks after the examination. Indeed, patients are present when pictures are produced, shown and interpreted on the job. After an ultrasound examination during which the radiologist explained hardly anything, the patient told me:

> P   I did not really see anything. Most of the time I was lying on my side. And then, they did not really tell me anything. They were just talking to each other. And then when they are whispering like that, you think, oh, maybe they have found something. But then he said: everything looks fine. Then I thought: well, then it must be okay.

What doctors say during and immediately after examinations may be similar to, but also rather different from the results that attending physicians communicate to their patients. A malignant-looking tumor may turn out to be benign or a blood test may indicate a normal looking bile duct to contain gallstones anyway. Coincidental findings that do not address the applicant's request are often mentioned during an examination, but might not be included in the report, or in the eventual consultation. Misunderstandings may arise about a fluoroscopy assistant saying that "the pictures look fine", referring to the quality of the prints rather than to the condition of the depicted body. Moreover, during examinations many doctors tend to use professional language that is largely incomprehensible to patients, whereas an attending physician tries to translate findings into more common-sense terms. However, physicians' comments on images during and after an examination, like "You see it is a bit red here, that means it is infected", or "This is fluid you see, because it is black", can contribute to patients' perceptions of real-time images as well.

As I argued earlier, diagnoses are rarely based on the report of a single imaging event. Consultations are usually not about the results of a particular examination; they are about the (possible) diagnosis suggested by the results, whether or not in combination with other data, and about possibilities for treatment or the necessity of follow-up. Sometimes a physician has requested various examinations and combines all results before proposing a diagnosis. In other cases, the result of a single examination is shared with a patient first to set a trajectory of further diagnostic or therapeutic action.

A patient's visit to the doctor is the final stage in professional translations of medical images. For patients it is one among several transformations that contribute to their incorporation of real-time imaging. The following case story illustrates this point.

A week after she underwent a colonoscopy, I accompany Mrs. Remmers on a visit to her attending surgeon. Since she had surgery for colon cancer eleven years ago, Mrs. Remmers has a check-up every three years. Her attending physician, the surgeon, does not perform endoscopic examinations himself. He got the results, including the lab findings about samples of polyps taken during the examination, from his colleague who did the colonoscopy. He tells Mrs. Remmers about the results:

D	Mmm, they were adenomous with some dysplasia. It must be removed entirely, before it turns into something nasty again.
MR	That is okay. As long as I will not need a stoma.
D	Oh no, they just need to remove that polyp.
MR	They told me to come back for a small examination.
D	Yes, that is a good idea. They look at the last eighty centimeters, and they can remove all polyps.
MR	It was not malignant, was it?
D	It will become malignant.

Two months later, I am in the same consultation room again, with the same surgeon
and with Mrs. Remmers. I met Mrs. Remmers in the waiting room half an hour earlier,
where she tells me that she had surgery for breast cancer less then a week ago. A
tumor had been found during a regular check-up, some weeks after I had last met her.
I have come to see Mrs. Remmers to accompany her on her visit to the doctor to hear
the results of her follow-up sigmoidoscopy. The endoscopist has told her already that
the polyp had been successfully removed, and that it was not malignant. The visit to
her attending surgeon, however, is largely dedicated to planning future treatment for
the breast cancer. Mrs. Remmers agrees on having radiotherapy, but strongly refuses
chemotherapy, since she does not "want to spend the rest of my life lying sick in bed".

Endoscopic pictures eventually only play a minor role in Mrs. Remmers' medical trajectory.
The only thing she wants is to recover from cancer and to prevent it from coming back. It is
the surgeon who is able to connect the results of the endoscopic examinations to her present
condition; his translations render the images important for Mrs. Remmers.

There are two moments when professionals' and patients' translations of real-time
images actually meet: when the images are produced (the imaging event) and when the results
are communicated (the consultation). When the trajectories meet, differences between them
are articulated yet their mutual shaping becomes apparent as well. Whereas during an
examination a patient's body presence is produced as a real-time referent for the imaging
event, during a consultation we witness the attempt to coordinate the different referent-bodies
that have emerged from physicians' and patients' translation trajectories into a suitable action
plan.

From screens to lived bodies

In real-time medical images, medical translations cross the trajectory of patients. Patients
engage in their own translations of imaging events. Professional translations of images into
medical knowledge and actions can be part of patients' trajectories, yet what is mediated in
the latter is embodied experience and identity. I return to Mr. Coenen to illustrate this point.

After having observed Mr. Coenen's ultrasound examination, I talk to him about the
examination and about his illness. He tells me that he has known for almost twenty

years that he has polycystic kidney disease. Back then, ultrasound was used for the
diagnosis, but Mr. Coenen does not remember whether he actually saw ultrasound
images of his kidneys. Lately Mr. Coenen has suffered from increased hypertension
and fatigue, identified by relatives and himself as possible signs of a decline in his
kidney functions. In an attempt to describe the likely condition of Mr. Coenen's
kidneys, his attending physician used a powerful metaphor.

MC	He (the attending physician, MR) said a kind of sponge, with small holes, with liquid-filled follicles. That is how he explained it. I did not remember that from the previous time (the ultrasound examination twenty years ago, MR), but then I did not really pay attention. That is different now.
MR	And now, did it look like you expected?
MC	It looked much worse than I imagined. The holes are much larger than I expected. I am a bit shocked actually. And then in the liver, she found some cysts there as well, I did not know about it.

The ultrasound images made a deep impression on Mr. Coenen. He was looking for a
sponge, yet the monitor showed him something different. Now that his kidneys did not
look like a sponge, with small holes, but were actually more hole than tissue, Mr.
Coenen felt that his condition was worse than he thought. The physician, however, was
less concerned with the number and sizes of the cysts but rather with the size of the
kidneys. The kidneys were too large to fit on the screen and could not be measured.
Mr. Coenen for his part was not impressed by that finding. He knew already that his
kidneys were large, because his doctor had felt that during a physical examination.

When the radiologist also located several cysts in Mr. Coenen's liver during
the same examination, Mr. Coenen was worried at first. He was then reassured by the
doctor who explained that a small number of little cysts is no cause for concern and
that people who are prone to having cysts in one organ are more likely to have them in
other organs as well. After the examination Mr. Coenen explained to me how he
experienced the images of his liver differently than the images of his kidneys:

> You see a liver (...), but actually I cannot really imagine it. She just tells me: this is the
> liver (...). But the kidneys, yes, they are easy to recognize. Well, not really recognize.
> You know that it is the thing with the holes in it, but you do not really see the shape of
> a kidney as you imagine it. At least, I do not.

Whereas Mr. Coenen had a framework for watching images of his kidneys – the doctor's image of a sponge – he did not have it for images of his liver.

In this story, the images showed that something was the matter, both to the radiologist and to Mr. Coenen. The nature of that matter, however, or the referent of the images, was different. Whereas the radiologist looked for clinically relevant information in the light of dialysis and transplantation by focusing on the size of the kidneys, Mr. Coenen compared the size and amount of the cysts to the interiorized image of a sponge in order to understand how ill he actually was. And where the liver was just another organ to visualize for the radiologist, for Mr. Coenen it was an unknown body part, unlike his kidneys.

To describe Mr. Coenen's real-time imaging experiences, I have presented part of his own narrative. In interpretative anthropology, narrative is generally considered to be the condition for experience. To become an experience, perceptions, thoughts, feelings or events need to be part of a narrative, or plot (cf. Desjarlais 1996). Many anthropological studies of illness study experience in terms of representations, interpretation and meaning (e.g. Kleinman 1988, Mattingly and Garro 2000). Patients' narratives, however, do not disclose how imaging technologies actually mediate embodied experience. Experiences are obviously shaped by the ways in which they are expressed but cannot be reduced to their expressions.

Inspired by phenomenology, anthropologists have described illness narratives also as constitutive of experience, claiming that narratives reconstitute objectified medical bodies as embodied selves. Yet a narrative approach has few tools to address what I have called productions of bodily presence in chapter 4. It addresses issues of representation and meaning production primarily in discursive terms, whereas embodied experience is both discursive and material. An anthropological, narrative approach to the spin-off of medical imaging into patients' embodied existence implies a bias towards concepts and reflections and leaves translations of bodily presence unattended. A constructivist description of translations includes the material and perceptual dimensions of embodiment and illness.

Translations of illness and disease

The preceding description of medical knowledge production, doctor-patient communication and patients' experiences in terms of *translation* points to Bruno Latour's concept of 'circulating reference' as an alternative for a representational epistemology, introduced in chapter 2. I extend this concept to describe both the production of medical knowledge through the objectivation of patients' bodies as well as the production of embodied experience through their subjectivation. The experience of being ill is a 'circulating referent' (Latour 1999a: 69) rather than a relation between a particular person and her or his body.

Illness, however, is not simply a subjective circulating capacity. It cannot be detached from the circulating referent that anthropologists have called *disease*: the medical-professional objectivation of a body's condition. The work of doctors is constitutive for patients' experience. When described separately, the production of medical knowledge can easily be contrasted to the enactment of illness: one trajectory involves the translation of images into written language, via a reading of images as data-sets; in the other trajectory, images are rather read as pictures and translated into narrative expressions of experience. Considering the trajectories as being in line rather than parallel, offers an alternative to dualist descriptions in terms of object/subject, knowledge/experience and disease/illness. The production of disease is part of the "ongoing, shifting dialogue between professional discourses, public narratives and personal lifeworlds" (Persson et al. 2003: 411) in which illness is enacted as a referent that makes "experiences and actions intelligible to self and to others" (Persson et al. 2003: 411).

An understanding of patients' experiences as well as doctors' knowledges in terms of circulating reference shows how capacities of bodies that have often been described as fundamentally different, actually result from continuous *intra-actions* (cf. Barad 1996: 179). The opposition between objective disease and subjective illness reflects a distinction between different sources of data: the techno-visual disclosure of the physical interior on the one hand, and the discursive analysis of patients' narratives on the other. My analysis of technological mediations of embodiment starts neither from the body that people have nor from the body they are, but shows how 'disease' and 'illness' are co-enacted in a particular practice.

Image incorporations

Since the narrative expressions usually studied by anthropologists only partially convey embodied experience, psychologists and phenomenologists have complemented narrative analysis with the study of *body images*, described in chapter 2. Body images include perceptions of, attitudes to and beliefs about one's own body in relation to others. Narratives are "part of the images people have of themselves"(Ochberg in Hydén 1997: 50), yet body images are more than narratives. Body images are translations of sensory perceptions into explicit or implicit mental representations. Jacques Lacan's analysis of the so-called mirror stage has shown that the mirror is crucial to the constitution of the body image as an integrated part of one's body (Lacan 1953).

Mirror images present a body's exterior appearance. Most people recognize themselves when they look into a mirror. The mirror shows the whole of the outside body, only partly visible without a mirror. The exterior body is also familiar through photos, videos and through other people's reactions to it. Real-time images, however, show parts of the body that are usually hidden from the eye. They present parts of one's body that usually recede from conscious experience as being one's own. I have observed examinations which mainly aimed at visualizing parts of patients' digestive and urinary systems, like kidneys, livers, spleens, intestines, bladders, and gallbladders. The interior body parts that medical images represent are "a matter of mystery and speculation" to most people (Helman 2001: 16). For the most part, visceral phenomena are unavailable to one's conscious awareness and control. Real-time medical imaging technologies transform how people perceive their bodies. Through mirror-like images, the absent body can be included in people's body images. Describing real-time imaging as a 'monitor stage' more or less analogous to the mirror stage (cf. Lajer-Burckhart 1997: 191) may contribute to an account of technological mediations of body image.

Body images are representations which are supposedly more embodied than narratives are. Yet such a representational concept does not allow for an understanding of embodied experience 'in practice'. Like narratives, body images only allow for an analysis of embodied experience through its expressions. My comparison of real-time medical images to mirror images does not prelude an analysis of transforming body images, but of the production of *image-bodies*. Real-time images and mirror images are alike in their simultaneous transformation of bodies as image, spectator and actor. Real-time imaging presents the interior body as an image, something that is an object of sensory perception yet differs from the body that perceives it. It is what Don Ihde has called an image-body. The image-body is a representation of one's own body, informed and shaped by culture, that does not coincide with the here-body that is the seat of sensory perception (Ihde 2002: 5).

Real-time medical images and mirror images produce similar image-bodies. An analysis of embodied experience in terms of narratives or body images cannot cover the similar material and perceptual impact of mirror images and real-time images that I have described as *presence* in chapter 4. The question is how such real-time presences are incorporated, i.e. translated into embodied experiences of a here-body, the embodied subject that is moving, perceiving, feeling and being-in-the-world (Ihde 2002: xi). In chapter 4, I have described attachments of here-bodies to image-bodies, concluding that they are intricately intertwined in the production of real-time medical images. Their simultaneous presence is disrupted once the examination is over. Physical bodies and material images are separated from their context of production. They end up in various new contexts: the translation trajectories that I have described in the first section of this chapter. In those trajectories four related categories of image-bodies emerge as referents for real-time imaging events: the *medical body* which is constructed in professional translations, the *transparent body* resulting from interferences of medical and media technologies, the *spectacular body* the patient has watched on the monitor, and the *lived body*, which is actively engaged in the imaging event as an embodied spectator and actor.

The medical body

The first translation trajectory that I have described earlier in this chapter has been the professional chain of translations: from real-time images to stills and prints, to spoken words, written texts and numbers. The body that is constructed as the referent for real-time medical images in this trajectory is a *medical body*. The imaging report coordinates a variety of visual and non-visual data into a stable referent-body that can be an object of diagnosis and treatment. In chapter 3, I described the request form for an examination as a coordinating device as well: it coordinated distributed agencies of machines, physicians, patients and bodies into a potential image. The body that is eventually presented in the imaging report, however, is not the body that has been anticipated by the request form. It has been affected by the simultaneous production of body's and image's presence during the examination. Although real-time productions of presence are removed from the imaging report as much as possible, the report carries their traces.

Compared to written reports, doctors' verbal observations during an examination usually contain more informalities, uncertainties and inconsistencies, like "this could be …" or "this might fit …". Although in written reports one also finds phrases such as "this may represent" or "this fits closely to", most uncertainties and associative tinkering has disappeared. The same holds for aesthetic and normative qualifications, which do not appear in final reports. Doctors may talk about beautiful pictures, when for example the contrast is very high, or when it shows an uncommon lesion. Sometimes, however, physicians include information that 'having been there' has granted them in an examination report.[74] The endoscopy report of a patient with a chronic bowel infection, for example, states that the examination went smoothly despite an anxious patient.

I mentioned before that real-time images are considered to be relatively subjective sources of information according to medical standards. Patients sometimes witness how 'objective' information is being produced.

I observed a surgeon communicating the results of a colonoscopy and an MRI-scan to a patient during a consultation. A malignant tumor had been removed from her colon a year earlier and her liver had been checked because some irregularities had been seen during an ultrasound examination, which was requested to check for possible metastasis. The colonoscopy looked normal now and the liver lesions seemed relatively innocent. Yet the surgeon proposed regular check-ups of the colon as well as of the liver. Since the patient was a bit claustrophobic she asked whether the latter could be done by means of ultrasound, since the lesions had also been detected with that technology. The surgeon explained why he preferred an MRI:

> Ultrasound is good for diagnosis, but not to check whether the lesions have increased in size or not. Besides, an ultrasound is more individual, it depends very much on who performs it, because it yields moving images. Not everyone is equally good at that. MRI is independent, and can better be compared.

The supposed subjectivity of ultrasound is related to its real-timeness. For images to be objective, they need to be intersubjectively comparable. Real-time images only make sense to the physician involved in making them: their referent is the examination event rather than a body-object. What is striking in the professional assessment of real-time imaging as subjective, is its contrast with lay perceptions of real-time images as 'live television'. For patients, it may seem that for physicians real-time images are means to see *through*: windows to bodily interiors. However, doctors emphasize their hermeneutic relation to images and bodies and consider images as tools to see the body *by* (cf. Verbeek 2005: 126).

---

[74] Barry Saunders describes how in the conference room, the (resident) readers of images are often not directly familiar with the clinical circumstances of the case on view. When a resident has been involved in the acquisition of an image, or in its primary reading, some things are easier to understand. 'Having been there' provides the reader with a special authority (Saunders forthcoming).

The medical body that patients meet during examinations and consultations is very different from their body in everyday experience. It is an object of textual and numerical interpretation rather than sensory or even visual perception. Differences between professional translations of images during the examination and afterwards during the consultation may result in alienating experiences. During an endoscopy, for instance, there may have been intensive discussion about the supposed abnormality of a polyp between physician and assistant, whereas the message of the attending physician a few weeks later may simply be that 'the examination showed that nothing is wrong with your colon". Either one of the two bodies fits the patient's perception: either he feels that something is wrong or he feels okay. Alienation then, either during the examination or after the consultation, results from a mismatch between embodied self-perception and objectified knowledge. Not the images alienated the patient from her or his body, but their translations. Real-time imaging renders the doctor's work transparent, rather than a patient's own body. When real-time discussions and ultimate diagnosis match, however, a strong identification of the patient with the images may be the result of imaging, as I will argue in one of the following subsections. The objectified bodies that physicians refer to in their production and reading of images may become part of patients' own bodies.

The transparent body

Links between medical technologies and media-technologies in the contemporary western world have resulted in a widespread ideal of a transparent and modifiable human body (Van Dijck 2005). Through newspapers, magazines and television shows, people have increasingly become used to medical language, doctors' work and to the icons of modern biomedicine: radiological and other medical images of the interior body. With the transfer of medical images to the public domain, the interior body has become a "bioscape" for non-professionals (Sawchuk 2000: 11). As cultural icons, medical images have become metaphors for particular bodily and mental states, such as pregnancy (Mitchell 2001) and depression or schizophrenia (Dumit 2004). Metaphors are not merely rhetorical instruments, but powerful epistemological devices by which people understand the world (Sontag 1991). The blurring of media images and medical images has resulted in a conception of illness situated inside a body, something that can be visualized by technological means. Patients implicitly compare media images of interior bodies to their own experiences during an examination, as in the following example.

After a diverticulitis (infected pouches in the intestinal lining, part of Mr. Breuls'
colon has been surgically removed three years ago. He has come for a check-up
sigmoidoscopy.

MR   The idea of looking inside your own body, how special is that?

MB   Well, they have those instruments these days. Whether you see it on
        television or here directly from yourself...

MR   That doesn't make much of a difference? Whether it is your own body or that
        of someone else on television?

MB   No.

MR   It does not feel differently? I can imagine, I mean, it is your own body.

MB   No, I do not experience it that way.

For Mr. Breuls the pictures on the monitor refer to a generic body that he recognizes from
TV, rather than to his own interior. The possibility to identify and locate disease by means of
medical images has become part of the standard lay perception of medicine and medical
practice. Paradoxically, real-time images that are relatively hard to reduce to two-dimensional
inscriptions for doctors and therefore are the weakest in terms of medical evidence, seem
particularly powerful in disseminating the idea of a transparent body among patients.

The transparent body is a mix of medical images and media images that constitutes a
macro-perceptual frame for those involved in real-time medical imaging (cf. Van Dijck 2005:
12). It is a cultural construct rather than a medical ideal. Earlier I have described how
professional translations of real-time imaging events do not start from pre-existing bodies and
visual representations. The production and interpretation of real-time images in practice is a
contingent, dynamic adjustment process in which bodies and images are enacted as fitting
entities. That complexity and messiness, however, tends to get lost in media translations of
medical imaging that enter the examination room with patients and with doctors. The
possibility to watch the monitor suggests to patients that there is something to be seen and
recognized.

When I observed ultrasound, fluoroscopy or endoscopy examinations I repeatedly
heard "Hey, will I be on TV?" or words of similar import, when patients saw the monitor in
the examination room. In chapter 4, I mentioned the perceptual similarity between real-time
medical imaging and live television. Like live television broadcasts, real-time images have an
aura of immediacy that other (still and stored) medical images lack. They appear immediately
upon their acquisition, suggesting direct access to the body 'as it really is'. Endoscopic color
images have a particularly realistic appearance. The 3D moist structures, red and blue vessels,

yellow excrements, and flowing blood after a biopsy, are more reminiscent of the body's fleshiness than the fussy black and white shapes of an ultrasound. Real-time imaging suggests an embodiment relation between doctor and imaging device.

From available analyses of real-time medical imaging in the field of visual culture, one might conclude that most lay experiences with medical images are through "biotourism" (Sawchuk 2000: 11) enabled by the mediatization and cultural dissemination of medical images. However, most of the patients I observed had seen medical images before during or after a medical examination of their own body or that of a relative or friend. The popularization of medical images is not merely the result of the mediatization of such images (Van Dijck 2005), but more and more of the growing number of people who have come acquainted to such images of their own body. What appears as transparent in magazines and on television is 'the generic body' rather than a particular patient's own body. The media image of the transparent body, however, informs patients' bodies lying on examination tables to undergo real-time medical imaging, in a way that is comparable to the mirror's role in conditioning that experience, described in the previous chapter.

The spectacular body

Technologies that on the one hand have been described as contributing to a transparent body actually do the opposite for many patients. Real-time medical images transform body parts that hitherto were absent from experience into unknown shapes and structures that seem unrelated to the ways in which patients perceive their bodies sensorily and introceptively. In the following fragment, the patient presents himself as a mere spectator of the body appearing on the screen.

> *Mr. Habets asked his general practitioner to be referred for an endoscopic check-up of his sigmoid. Although his complaints are likely to be due to hemorrhoids, he wants to make sure it is nothing more serious. After the examination I asked him how he experienced the examination.*

> MH   It is the second time I see this. I had never imagined an intestine would look like this. I just thought it was a small tube with a large balloon on top. But if you see, through such a camera... then one sees how ingenious it all is. You cannot really understand how it all works.

> MR   Did it look very different from what you expected?

MH   Yes, it is all very special. When you think that you eat, you digest that, the waste products are processed and then flow through that tube, through the anus, it comes out. That is ingenious, a mystery really, isn't it?

MR   It is special indeed.

MH   The body is a mystery. The ticking of the heart, the seeing of the eyes, that's so unbelievable!

The endoscopic pictures indeed showed Mr. Habets that apart from the hemorrhoids, his sigmoid looked perfectly normal. But more than that, the images provided him with a view into the ingenious machinery of his body. The pictures filled him with awe for the visual spectacle, so different from his body as he knew it.

Images can be more powerful than sensory perceptions. The Dutch anthropologist Anne-Mei The has described how radiologists use X-rays to convince patients who do not feel very ill they have lung cancer and need to start chemotherapy. During and after the therapy, when patients feel much more ill than at the time of diagnosis, X-rays are used to show patients that their condition is improving. Although their cancer is incurable, the images make patients optimistic about their chances for recovery. They rather trust the images to tell them how ill they are than the sensory perceptions of their own bodies (The et al. 2003). This example illustrates how the image that I call the spectacular body can be reinforced by the image of the medical body communicated by doctors. This mechanism can also be observed in the case of Mr. Habets whom I just quoted. He also said that

MH   First, looking inside your own body is very interesting. It is like science-fiction. But I think it is also psychologically important. Maybe not for everyone, but for me it is. That you can see any time what is wrong with you. That the diagnosis they come up with, that you have seen it... that they cannot make it up. That you can convince yourself. That is, if they give a full explanation of what they are doing, and they did that.

For Mr. Habets it is through the doctor's explanation that the images come to refer to his own body. Despite the double objectivation of his body – through his own spectatorship and through the doctor's reading – Mr. Habets is attached to what he sees on the monitor. The real-timeness of the images, however, is not a main constituent of attachment here. It is rather through his emotional responses that the images affect Mr. Habets as a person.

Technologies and practices of modern medicine have been described by philosophers and social scientists as a source of alienation and a move *away* from patients' own experiences and embodied selves (e.g. Duden 1993b, Leder 1990, Toombs 1992). In their analyses of medical practices, sociologists and anthropologists have frequently opposed objective medical conditions that "can be directly read from the body or discovered through laboratory tests" (Baszanger 1998: 145) to experiences of pain and illness that are private, personal and only indirectly accessible through patients' narratives. Diagnostic technologies are then opposed to subjective expressions of experience, either explicitly in terms of alienation, or implicitly in terms of knowledge versus experience. Rather than about oppositions, however, my story has been about diverging and converging trajectories. The chains of translation described in the first section of this chapter involve different actors and produce different bodies as referents from real-time imaging, yet they all include the stage of simultaneous presence of body and image in real-time.

Introspections: images of one's own body

For some patients watching real-time medical images is like watching a television show. For many, however, the set-up of a real-time imaging event constitutes a direct relation between the images on the monitor and their own bodies, as in the case of Mr. Theunissen introduced in chapter 2.

> *Mr. Theunissen has suffered from a chronic bowel infection for almost twenty years. He regularly undergoes a colonoscopy to check his condition, especially when he experiences pain or other symptoms.*
>
> MR   Did you ever see those kind of images, except for those of yourself? On television maybe?
>
> MT   Okay, but then it is just an examination you would be watching, not your own.
>
> MR   If you see those images, you know that: this is my body, this is me?
>
> MT   Yes. You feel that, you know? You feel that tube right here in your guts. You can feel approximately where they are with that tube.

In chapter 4, I quoted Mr. Theunissen to illustrate the production of the body as simultaneously an object of a patient's visual and of his sensory perception. I argued that the simultaneity of seeing and feeling is constitutive for a particular mode of embodied presence during a real-time imaging event. I come back to it here, because it shows that the transparent media body is not simply transferred to personal experience, but is made part of a complex configuration of knowledge-producing and experience-evoking actors.

In chapter 4 I quoted Mr. Theunissen saying that he knew the white spots that appeared on the monitor to be signs of infection; he said that from what he felt, he could infer what the endoscopic images would show. Mr. Theunissen presented himself as an informed spectator, an object of visual and sensory perception and an object of medical examination at the same time. In his story about the imaging event, the four modes of attachment identified in chapter 4 are integrated: the professional real-time readings, the simultaneous visual and haptic perception of one's interior, one's active subjection to the requirements of imaging and also the emotions about him being ill that were evoked by each examination, as described in chapter 2. The translation of those modes of attachment that were simultaneously present in real-time, can only partly be expressed by narrative means. The composite image has become part of the body that Mr. Theunissen is.

Michel Callon and Vololona Rabeharisoa have described how objectivations of the bodies of people with muscular dystrophy by means of a mirror, transform the ways in which that body is able to perceive and act as a result of the constant going back and forth between being a body and having a body:"(i)t is the miracle of the mirror which makes these two experiences possible at the same time and makes this essential tension visible" (Callon and Rabeharisoa n.d.). The simultaneous real-time presence of a body as an image and as one's own lived body characteristic for real-time medical imaging, similarly translates bodily presence into embodied experience.

Patients with a chronic condition undergo medical examinations on a regular basis. They become acquainted to pictures of their interior body and integrate them in their body images. During an interview, Mr. van Norden, who suffers from a chronic bowel infection, explained that watching the images is interesting because they show what is behind the symptoms so familiar to him: pain, blood and diarrhea. Seeing the images helps him to understand what is going on, he said. Similar remarks were made by several other patients.. Mr. Coolen, who attends his wife's endoscopy and has undergone similar examinations himself, summarized this experience concisely when he advised his wife to watch the monitor during the examination:

> The more you see, the more you know, the more you are informed, and the better you can cope with it.

Images do not merely represent one's body: they transform one's embodied existence.

The possibility to watch real-time images on a monitor provides many patients with a sense of control in a situation that is characterized by uncertainty and uneasiness. Physicians often mention this as an advantage of showing patients real-time pictures. I asked Mr. and Mrs. Coolen what they actually got from watching the monitor.

Mr. C   I was much more involved, for sure.

M   How do you mean?

Mr. C   It is only positive. It is not abstract, it is concrete, it is just reality.

Mrs. C   You see what is happening to you, what they are doing with you, and that is nice, sure.

The possibility for patients to watch the real-time images affords a particular mode of synecdoche, meaning that an objectified body part can come to stand for oneself, since one is able to relate to it as an actor (cf. Cussins 1998). Whether or not watching the monitor during the examination provides patients with meaningful agency over the examination or their own bodies, depends on the extent to which patients are provided with the means to read the images. Doctors' guidance through the images gives patients a sense of control over a situation generally considered to be beyond their personal command. That situation is not limited to the examination, but also includes the experience of being ill or at risk of illness.

However, the benefits of watching medical images of your own body is doubted by some patients, among whom Mr. Hendriks who had an ultrasound because of abdominal pain.

MH   In itself it is progress, that hospitals and doctors try to be more open about what is going on. But the openness has limits as well: you (a doctor, MR) should tell something that someone else (the patient, MR) can understand. But when someone is not able to understand what you say, simply because he or she lacks knowledge, well, then you (the doctor, MR) are speaking a kind of magical language. That is not useful.

Watching real-time images can reinforce a loss of control in patients when they lack a meaningful frame of reference. Patients are then unable to link the represented body to their embodied self. The objectivation of one's body then results in alienation. Some patients do not consider that problematic whatsoever. In chapter 4, I described patients who were not at all keen on watching the monitor during an examination. Some explained their choice not to watch by referring to the doctor's attitude ("They do not explain anything, so I do not understand it anyway"), others were happy to leave the doctor with the responsibility of watching the images. They are only interested in the results. After a colonoscopy under sedation, I heard a patient say to the endoscopist that she had not seen anything, but that was "okay, because I do not need to know everything".

Not all real-time imaging events result in patients' identification with images. The complex nature of image-mediated embodied experience becomes particularly apparent when patients' feelings contradict doctors' findings. Mr. Geels, who was introduced in chapter 2, told me about the fluoroscopic examination of his colon.

> MG   The doctor pushed me on the belly and then I said: "Ouch, that hurts". And he said: "That pain is there, but we do not see anything". That is what he said. I said: "Well, I do not understand it". He said: "Yes, it is different for you. There is pain, but we do not see anything." So now I just wait for the final results.

The doctor could not see the cause of the pain that Mr. Geels felt. The examination resulted in what has been called *disembodiment*, or *alienation* between the body-as-self and the body-as-object (Young 1997: 4-5). The eventual report of Mr. Geels' fluoroscopy indeed stated that no abnormalities had been found. An earlier colonoscopy resulted in the same conclusion. Mr. Geels was convinced something was wrong and considered going to another hospital for a second opinion. His case shows that real-time imaging sometimes does not produce the expected images of a patient's own body. However, there is nothing in the nature of the technologies or the images that constitutes alienation, and neither is there something essential about real-time imaging technologies that produces transparency or identification. Real-time imaging can produce synecdoche: images representing a patient's condition. Alienation, caused by contradictory visual and sensory perceptions, is a possible outcome as well.

From image to body

During real-time imaging, the referent for live images on the monitor is the imaging event: the temporal and spatial configuration of doctor, patient and machine collectively producing bodies as objects and subjects of imaging and sensory perception. As soon as the imaging event is over, images enter two translation trajectories: a trajectory of professional translation into medical findings by doctors and a trajectory of translation into patients' embodied experience articulated in narratives and body images. Those epistemological and phenomenological translations diverge, yet they are connected in the same material imaging practices of examination and consultation. A patient's experienced body is contaminated by "the body set up by medical knowledge" (Akrich and Pasveer 2004: 81). In most cases, images require an expert's interpretation to be meaningful to patients. Professional translations may add to patients' knowledge and command of their own bodies.

Don Ihde's concept of *image-bodies* helps to describe categories of referents for real-time imaging events emerging in physicians' and patients' translations (Ihde 2002). It is only in patients' and professionals' translations that real-time images obtain a stable, yet composite referent: an image-body. The image-body is the object of embodied experience. Transformations of image-bodies by real-time medical imaging include the connection of image-body to here-body. What happens to image-bodies in professional and patients' translations affects one's own acting, perceiving body as well.

'Image-body' describes the connection as well as the separation between one's body as an object of perception and oneself as a perceiving subject. It is your own body as you can see it yourself. That visual perception is mediated by mental images from the media or previous experiences, by the technology used to produce real-time images, by professional translations and by the physical sensation triggered by imaging. Both professionals' and patients' translations of those visual perceptions into knowledge and embodied experience are informed by patients' simultaneous embodied presence as object, actor, and spectator during a real-time imaging event. Those translations include the 'subjective' professional reading of ephemeral real-time images, the implicit or explicit comparisons of clinical images to media images and the connections between what patients see and what they feel.

Patients' experiences of their body during and after real-time imaging are situated along a continuum stretching from complete disembodiment to full identification of the images with one's embodied self. In chapter 2, I claimed that existing anthropological and sociological frames separate disease from illness, object from subject, body from person and knowledge from experience. A focus on productions of embodied presence, as advocated in chapter 4, shows the irrelevance of common dualisms in practice. Disease and illness, object and subject, body and person, knowledge and experience are co-produced during a real-time imaging event. After the event, physicians and patients objectify the images and the bodies that are produced as their referents. What is objectified however, is not a pre-existing physical entity represented by moving pictures, but an image-body that is present as an image and a perceiving body at the same time. The translation of presence into embodied experience implies transformations of subjectivity.

Despite their simultaneous presence during an imaging event, image and body do not coincide. The difference, or 'écart',[75] between perceiving and perceived body in a real-time imaging event does not necessarily result in an experience of alienation, however. Some patients include real-time images – i.e. the translations of real-time imaging events – in their body images. Even for me as a mere observer, having watched the images of patients' intestines affected how I perceived my own body. Eating ice-cream shortly after I had observed several duodenoscopies,[76] I imagined in endoscopic pictures the position of the cold substance I felt moving down my intestines. Whether permanently or not, real-time imaging may affect how patients perceive their own bodies afterwards. Physical sensations can bridge the space between image and own body. Thus technological representations of interior bodies can provide patients with an unusual "visual experience of the self" that brings along "the advent of a new mode of relatedness to self" (Merleau-Ponty 1962 in Weiss 1999: 37).

Real-time imaging technologies mediate embodied experience, which includes the production of medical reference and patients' agency. That is, images are actively involved in the construction of bodies as subjects and objects of perception and experience. I use the term 'mediation' in the way of Latour, to describe how real-time imaging transforms how bodies are present to people as well as how people live and act as bodies (Verbeek 2005: 147-8; Latour 1999a). In other theoretical frames and in every-day language, however, the concept of mediation tends to describe the hermeneutic dimension of experience rather than the perceptual, material dimension of existence and agency (cf. Latour 2002: 250). Therefore, I prefer another expression coined by Latour to describe the work of real-time imaging in the formation of embodied experience: that of a body learning to be affected.

> When you enter into contact with hospitals, your 'rich subjective personality' is not reduced to a mere package of objective meat: on the contrary, you are now *learning to be affected* by masses of agencies hitherto unknown not only to you, but also to doctors, nurses, administration, biologists, researchers who add to your poor inarticulate body complete sets of new instruments (....) No subjectivity, no introspection, no native feeling can be any match for the fabulous proliferation of affects and effects that a body learns when being processed by a hospital (...).
> (Latour 2004: 227, italics MR).

---

[75] Cf. chapter 4, p. 96.
[76] Endoscopic examinations of the oesophagus. I watched several of those examinations in the initial stage of my fieldwork. Since patients are not able to watch the monitor during a duodenoscopy, however, I excluded the examination from my eventual sample.

In the translations of real-time imaging events by patients and physicians described in the present chapter, patients learn to be affected by the particular presence produced during an examination. Real-time imaging technologies trigger a series of translations of bodies and images into image-bodies, which function as objects of patients' embodied experience. Rather than being the material basis for the formation of an embodied identity, one's body is "an interface that becomes more and more describable as it learns to be affected by more and more elements" (Latour 2004: 206). The imaging devices, monitors, pictures, numbers, gestures, spoken words, reports, cultural images and sensory perceptions involved in a real-time imaging event are examples of such elements. Embodied experience is enacted in real-time imaging practice. It is a not a meaning, belief or interpretation, but a *proposition*. Latour uses this concept, coined by the philosopher Isabelle Stengers, as an alternative to the notion of statement, which stands for the representationalist idea of "statements referring to matters of fact through the fragile bridge of correspondence" (Latour 2004: 212). As I argued before, statements about embodiment are not able to provide access to embodied experience. Regarding the body as a proposition articulated in a real-time imaging event, however, presents embodiment as a material becoming rather than an interpreted state of being.

The notion of embodiment as a proposition, as 'learning to be affected', denies any distinction between an 'inside' self and an 'outside' body. It allows for an account of techno-visually mediated embodiment as 'subjective body-fashioning'.[77] Patients are capable of being a self and acting as oneself through the multiplication of their connections with 'outside' elements. In Latour's words: "you need to subscribe to a lot of subjectifiers to become a subject" (Latour 2005: 216). Real-time images are neither outside representations that suppress embodied experience nor are they immediate self-evident views inside oneself. The enactment of image-bodies in patients' and professionals' translations of real-time imaging events is a process in which patients actively learn to be bodies.

---

[77] This expression refers to the idea of 'objective self-fashioning' used by Joe Dumit to describe "how we take facts about ourselves – (about our bodies, minds, capacities, traits, states, limitations, propensities, and so on) – that we have read, heard, or otherwise encountered in the world and incorporate them into our lives" (Dumit 2004: 164). Whereas Dumit's concept attends to "the categories of the person built into facts" (Dumit 2004: 164), subjective body-fashioning refers to the ways in which objectivations of one's body transform embodied self-experience.

Illness in practice

Nearing the end of my analysis, I narrow the focus: from the ways in which *bodies* learn to be affected in real-time imaging practices to the more specific *experiences of illness and health* that my research question addresses. In the present and preceding chapters I have substantiated the claim that "technologies fundamentally shape people's experience of disease" (Verbeek 2006: 366). Real-time imaging mediates how for patients, their own bodies are present as sick or healthy. What makes their interference with illness experience fundamental, however, is that such hermeneutical mediations are intertwined with transformations of patients' active and material existence as healthy or ill.

The set-up of a real-time imaging event suggests that illness can be made visible. Examinations are often standard starting points in a diagnostic trajectory – when illness is suspected, one of the first things to do is have a look at the body's interior. Implicitly or explicitly inviting patients to watch the examination, doctors and monitors articulate the assumption that illness is visible. Spectators of real-time medical images, however, even when they are experienced or trained, do not see 'health' or 'illness'. They see shapes, colors, movements, codes and numbers. Physicians as well as patients engage in the active production of diagnostic information, body images and sensory perceptions as referents for the apparent visual clues. The translation of such referents into narratives is a material-discursive process, like the preparations described in chapter 3. Moreover, the mediating power of real-time images, described in chapter 4, transcends the borders of the examination room.

Illness is not something a body has or something a person is, nor is it what a body is or what a person has. Illness is a proposition rather than either a physical condition or a complex of meanings (Latour 2004: 212 ff.). It circulates as a potential referent of real-time images along the chains of reference performed before, during and after imaging events by patients, physicians, imaging devices, pictures, body parts and many other actors. Without technological interference, the interior body that possibly harbors illness is largely absent from a patient's conscious experience (Leder 1990).[78] The imaged body parts are hidden in one's interior and generally recede from sensory perception.

In chapter 2, I introduced Drew Leder's concept of dys-appearance, describing illness as a mode of bodily absence. I have argued, however, that illness is a particular articulation of

---

[78] The idea that health is 'the silence of organs' has also been articulated by George Canguilhem (cf. Mol 2006: 44).

a body's presence. How that presence has been produced is therefore constitutive for how illness is experienced. Real-time imaging technologies enable the production of a characteristic co-presence of image and body. Experiences of illness or health are enacted in translations of that co-presence into more or less stable referent-bodies. Real-time imaging technologies interfere in the space between a lived body and its representations. Whether real-time imaging contributes to an alienating experience of embodiment and illness or evokes patients' identification with particular image-bodies hinges on the (in)compatibility of physicians' and patients' translations in practice. Rather than reflecting a body's condition or estranging bodies from selves, real-time images are means of articulation through which bodies learn to be affected. The diffuse and contradictory experiences of patients taking part in real-time imaging events require a concept of illness that acknowledges and addresses the hermeneutic as well as the material and existential layers of embodiment.

6   Inside out: endographic conclusions

Real-time medical images exist only for a moment, yet it has taken me an entire book to describe their role in how people experience their bodies and their illnesses. Real-time medical imaging deserves that ample attention because of its special status in the visual opening of human bodies. It allows patients an unprecedented direct visual access to the inside of their bodies through pictures claiming to represent their interior. The possibility to watch images of their interior complicates patients' experience of their bodies. In a clinical setting, that experience often includes illness. Real-time imaging transforms the matter of patients' bodies (the bodies that patients perceive), their meaning (how patients perceive their bodies) and their agency (how patients act as bodies). Therefore, real-time medical imaging requires a reconceptualization of social-scientific notions of embodiment and illness.

As an ethnographer entering the worlds of radiology and endoscopy, I entered the bodies of patients. I looked with patients at pictures of their interiors. As an endographer, I traced how real-time images affect bodies as they are watched and watching, known and knowing, experienced and experiencing. Characteristic for real-time imaging is the constant going back and forth between image and body and between inside and outside. Visualizations neither replace other perceptions nor do they reduce a body to images: bodies and images are both actors as well as results of imaging.

The circulation of illness

Real-time medical imaging presents the human interior simultaneously as both object and subject of perception, knowledge and experience. Understood as a process, embodiment presents an alternative to the dualist idea of being and having a body. In the clinical practices I have described, real-time medical imaging devices and the pictures they produce are part of embodiment processes. I have focused on *illness* as a specific mode of embodiment. In social-scientific discourse, *illness* is an object of subjective experience ("I *am* ill') that is usually contrasted to *disease*, which is the object of professional medical knowledge production ("I *have* a disease'). The social-scientific notion of *illness* is an interpretative, hermeneutic concept to describe expressions of experience that are mostly narrative. Alternatively, I have analyzed *illness* as a mode of embodied experience circulating in clinical practices of real-time imaging.

Bruno Latour has introduced the concept of *circulating reference* as an alternative for a representationalist epistemology. Correspondences between the world and representations of phenomena in the world, result from scientific work rather than from a confrontation between a knowing subject and a given research object (Latour 1999a). I have analyzed clinical practices of real-time medical imaging along those lines. Since the objects of medical examinations are patients' bodies, I have included both patients' and physicians' referential work in my descriptions of real-time imaging practices. Whereas for medical professionals real-time imaging is an instrument of knowledge production, for patients it constitutes particular perceptions and experiences of their own bodies. The referent of that knowledge, perception and experience is (the presence or absence of) *illness*. I have presented *circulating reference* both as an alternative epistemology and as an alternative phenomenology. In various stages of translation in real-time imaging, the phenomenon 'illness' obtains multiple hermeneutic, material and existential layers.

Myths on trial

I studied chains of translations that link the bodies of patients to biomedical diagnoses leading to and following from real-time imaging events. Rather than describing medical images as representations, I have analyzed productions of bodies' presence. The co-presence of a patient's physical body and ephemeral pictures of parts of its interior affords modes of embodiment that put common analytical concepts and distinctions to the test. Among them is the idea of a *transparent body*. Although its immediacy suggests direct access to physical realities, I showed that real-time imaging involves translation rather than representation. Real-time imaging transforms as well as transfers the bodies of patients. Rather than being reduced to images, bodies are multiplied to include images. They become more rather than less (cf. Latour 2004: 227), opaque rather than transparent.

My analysis has also challenged the idea – which is somehow the opposite of the notion of a transparent body – of the essential strangeness of representations of one's body that result from a 'clinical gaze' (Foucault 1973). Real-time medical images do not represent bodies' interiors, but actively contribute to patients' bodies' *presence*. My story about real-time imaging has been neither a salvational nor an apocalyptic narrative about the blessings or dangers of medical technology. Whoever takes a close look at medical practices may notice that such grand oppositions are not very helpful in understanding what medicine and technology do with people and what people do with medicine and technology. Through a detailed analysis of *how* bodies and images are attached, I have differentiated the popular myth of the transparent body as well as that of alienating medicalization, and therewith also the contrast between those myths.

The chain of real-time imaging

The figure on the next page summarizes the structure of my argument. It presents technological, professional and patients' acts and transformations in real-time imaging as a chain of translations. As in Latour's graphical representation of circulating reference (1999a: 70), the different stages of translation are not directly linked, avoiding the suggestion of univocal relations. Every stage is at once 'matter' for the next translation as well as 'form' for the previous one. Each oval represents the dominant mode of embodiment in the various stages of a body's imaging trajectory, as discussed in the previous chapters. Although chapter 2 has primarily been written as an introduction to my main theoretical frames and concepts, the case studies included gave an impression of patients' entrance into a medical trajectory. It presented a first stage of transformation: from embodied illness experience to becoming an object of medical examination. Chapter 3 described the second stage: the collective embodiment of patients as object and instruments of real-time medical imaging – and by the same token their collective embodiment as spectators and sensing subjects. The translation of those prepared bodies into imaging event-networks was the focus of chapter 4. Finally, in chapter 5 I described how professionals' and patients' translations of those events become part of patients' embodied experience. In the stages of preparation, imaging and translation elaborated upon in chapters 3, 4 and 5, the configuration of a collective-body object, the production of a body's visual presence, and the phrasing of reports and diagnoses transform patients' embodied experience. The co-enactment of embodied objectivity and embodied subjectivity is represented by dotted lines in the following figure.

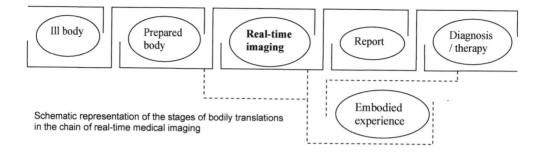

Schematic representation of the stages of bodily translations
in the chain of real-time medical imaging

The referent circulating along this chain is *illness*: the potential object of medical
examination and of embodied experience. An 'objective' finding or a subjective perception
are possible effects of tuning activity and passivity, seeing and feeling. At each step in the
chain, the referent of medical imaging is materially and discursively adjusted to the
requirements of a particular configuration of actors.

Interdisciplinary reflections

The enactment of illness experience in real-time medical imaging is too complex to be
described in terms of a single disciplinary framework. Using concepts and ideas from
medical anthropology, the sociology of health and illness, actor-network theory and (post-)
phenomenology, I have developed what could best be described as either an elaboration of
post-phenomenology or of actor-network theory. Whereas in chapter 3, I presented an ANT-
style analysis of patients' bodies as actor-networks, in chapter 5 I attempted to describe
experience as more than discursive subject position or narrative expression. Chapter 4
connected the two approaches in an analysis of real-time productions of bodily presence,
building on the prepared actor-networks and providing the basis for subsequent translations
into embodied experience.

The leading idea that a body, being subject as well as object of experience, does not
precede technological imaging but results from it, comes closest to the work of post-
phenomenologists. Postphenomenology, however, has not explicitly addressed medical
technologies so far. Moreover, I argue that an analysis of technologically mediated
embodiment requires an elaborate description of the formation of the networks in which

bodies emerge. Although people in their expressions of experience often distinguish between their body as a subject and as an object, in real-time imaging events the networks in which bodies emerge into presence cannot be empirically separated from people's relations with their own bodies. I take the complementarity of phenomenology and ANT a step further than post-phenomenologists have done. Whereas they acknowledge and demonstrate the value of ANT in the analysis of constructions of objectivity in a chain of translations, post-phenomenologists zoom in on relations between a maximum of three actors (person - technology - world, cf. Verbeek 2005: 170). A post-phenomenological analysis of real-time imaging would leave the black boxes of "the humans who experience and act, the mediating artifacts, and the humans and things that are experienced or dealt with" (Verbeek 2005: 166) closed, since it "is interested not so much in the networks of relations on the basis of which the mediating artifacts and the experiencing humans are present, but in the nature of the relations that human beings – thanks to these artifacts – can have to other humans and things" (ibid.). I have argued, however, that a meaningful understanding of technologically mediated human experience requires insight in the ways images and people are presented. Actor-network theory allows for descriptions of the conditions of experience and the forms it can take, moving beyond experience as a subject-object relation. It thus enables an analysis of how relations of mutual engagement become articulated in terms of subjects, object, representation, experience, perception or knowledge in the first place.

Whereas phenomenologists choose to put any presuppositions about what the world – or a body – is between brackets,[79] I have argued that phenomena can only be described in a context that is wider than the relation between directly involved entities. An analysis of technological mediations of embodied experiences of illness cannot be limited to patients, images and bodies, but includes the processes in which those actors have emerged. Bodies learn to see, feel, act and experience – in short: to be affected – in hybrid networks.

Distributed embodiment

My theoretical work contributes most significantly to medical anthropology, where the disease/illness dualism since its introduction has rarely been an issue, and where medical technology has been under-researched. Building on the strengths and responding to the

---

[79] This is called 'phenomenological reduction'.

weaknesses of the frames and vocabularies presented in chapter 2, I have developed a notion of illness as a mode of *distributed* embodiment.[80] Throughout this book I have described various distributions of embodiment in real-time imaging practices: among lived bodies, patients, intestines, kidneys, physicians, technological devices, pictures, reports, words and numbers. The idea of *distributed embodiment* summarizes my critique of hermeneutic distortions in medical anthropology, of the subject/object dualism in (post-) phenomenology and of ANT's bias towards agency. 'Distributed embodiment' is the result of 'bodies learning to be affected' (Latour 2004), a notion that I have introduced in chapter 5 to replace that of a 'mediated body'. The latter notion risks to be understood in terms of representation rather than agency, existence, and presence. Examples can be found in analyses of embodiment in the field of cultural studies and critical theory, where both embodiment and technology are put into discourse and treated as tropes or representations (cf. Hayles in Hansen 2000: vi).[81] The following table indicates the differences between the interpretative notion common in medical anthropology and cultural studies and the constructivist notion of embodiment developed throughout this book. Characteristic for the latter are three elements first introduced in the conceptual matrix in chapter 2: the *collective* nature of embodiment, the *material* and *agential* notion of experience and the constitutive role of *technology*. The notion of illness that follows from this frame is one of illness as an embodied experience not situated *inside* a body or a person, but enacted in collective processes of distributed embodiment.

Interpretative frame	Constructivist frame
Embodied identity	Embodied experience
Illness as meaning	Illness as experience
Representations	Productions and translations of presence
Discourse	Practice
Perception	Agency
Images	Imaging
Body-image	Image-body
Narrative	Matter
Body as condition	Body as proposition

[80] Cf. the concept of 'distributed cognition' (Hutchins 1995).
[81] The focus on issues of representation seems to be at odds with the usually explicit political agenda of scholarly work in this field, often referred to as 'identity politics'. Most analyses of embodiment seem to be detached from the material realities of the issues of study (e.g. transsexuality or disability) in the research field. Embodied identity is studied through the analysis of representations, meanings and concepts. A paradox arises: how to transform people's ways of doing by means of alternative vocabularies and ways of thinking that are merely discursive? A more radical realistic rethinking of embodiment seems more fruitful for political action. A constructivist notion of embodiment addresses the reality of living with an illness or a body, which a representationalist notion does not. Descriptions of the assemblage of the body in material-discursive practices (e.g. Barad 1998, Latour 2004) poses more of a challenge to existing frames and practices than conceiving the material body as a discursive construction (cf. Butler 1993).

Real-time imaging, articulate patients and the logic of care

Real-time imaging may not transform life and personhood as radically as for example genetics or neuroscience do, yet it does induce new modes of subjectivation. Moreover, real-time medical imaging embodies, articulates and problematizes certain central developments and values in contemporary biomedicine and western culture, like the mediatization of medicine (cf. van Dijck 2005) and the rise of an 'articulate patient'. Besides instrumental objectives like enhancing patients' compliance to examination requirements and subsequent therapy or further examinations, real-time imaging may fit normative objectives. Stimulating the rise of 'articulate patients' who are well-informed and make autonomous choices, can be such an objective. The possibility to share the professional clinical gaze by watching a monitor during an examination seemingly allows patients to be conscious, autonomous, critical consumers of medical services, like those described in the following quote about genetic medicine:

> (…) to make human individuality the object of positive knowledge is not 'subjection' in the sense of domination and the suppression of freedom – it is the *creation* of subjects that is at stake here. Today, as at the birth of clinical medicine, the sick person bears their illness with their corporeality and vitality – it is the body itself that has become ill. But this somaticization of illness did not, in fact, mandate the eternal passivity of the patient. In fact, clinical medicine, increasingly of the last half of the twentieth century, constituted the patient as an 'active' subject – one who must play their part in the game of cure. (Novas and Rose 2000: 489, italics in original)

The possibility to watch real-time images of one's own interior, however, does not automatically result in patients' active spectatorship and involvement. Let's for example take patients who choose not to watch the images. Although both patients and physicians usually present and understand it as an individual decision, the 'choice' whether or not to watch the monitor during an examination seems a logical outcome of the confrontation between many patients' image of omniscient techno-medicine and the lack of information of the possibilities and impossibility of real-time imaging before and during examinations. On the one hand, media images of medical technology have convinced many patients that their bodies are transparent for doctors. On the other hand, to understand anything themselves, many patients feel dependent on individual physicians' willingness and ability to explain what they see and do. Physicians who do not inform patients about the objectives, procedure and context of an examination may enforce the idea of a body that is transparent and manageable only for professionals. In short, real-time imaging is not merely involved in the performance of patients' bodies, but also in the performance of the clinic in which those bodies come to existence (cf. Berg and Bowker 1997: 514). Real-time imaging practices articulate an *apparatus of appearance* that includes hierarchies between medical specialties and imaging technologies and patients' alleged and actual roles in medical knowledge production.

For patients who do choose to watch the monitor, any claim about the contribution of real-time imaging to their empowerment would be empty, since patients are not explicitly being prepared for their role as spectators in real-time medical imaging events. The notion of distributed embodiment, which enables a more precise analysis of how patients are affected by real-time medical imaging than existing concepts, displays patients' possibly contradictory perceptions and experiences. For patients, what they see, hear and feel during a real-time imaging trajectory can be confusing and sometimes inconsistent. This book has presented a way to deal with that inconsistency primarily on a conceptual, theoretical level. All theoretical explorations, however, have been informed by empirical observations of real-time imaging practices. Its results could be relevant for those practices as well. The complexity of illness experience in real-time medical imaging may also require practical adjustments.

Physicians are usually unaware of the contradictory perceptions and experiences that real-time imaging may evoke in patients. When doctors present medical images to patients as representations of a state of affairs, they themselves produce a view of images as pictures depicting an objective reality, rather than communicating the interpreted nature of images. The whole set-up of clinical practice invites an appraisal of imaging and images as pictures rather than events, as reflections rather than interpretations, as reality rather than data to be interpreted. In their professional translations of real-time imaging events, physicians produce a more or less univocal referent. Patients, on the other hand, are confused by the multiple referents of real-time imaging they encounter, and in particular by contradictions between their own perceptions and physicians' translations. Indeed, many patients do feel reassured and secured by the possibility to 'see for themselves', underscoring its psychological importance. However, they are not adequately prepared for real-time imaging.

Patients are actively involved in material and cognitive preparations for their part as research object and instrument in a real-time imaging event, but they are not prepared for their role as spectator. By referring to their role as spectators, I do not mean to allude to possible emotional reactions, but to the lack of information about what real-time imaging technologies actually do with or in a body, about how they produce pictures and about the role of those pictures in diagnoses and therapies. Written and verbal information for patients before and during real-time imaging could contain more explicit reference to such aspects. Such information could raise patients' consciousness about the reductive implications of preparations and procedures and the limited diagnostic possibilities of imaging. It would require physicians to be more aware of patients' possibly contradictory experiences of real-time imaging.

However, arguing for more and better information to teach patients on how to watch and understand real-time medical images is too simple, as it remains doubtful how such information would actually boost patients' say in medical decision-making and contribute to their role as critical consumers and citizens. Notwithstanding the potentially profound impact of real-time imaging on patients' experiences of their bodies and their illnesses and on their interaction with medical professionals, the possibility to watch medical images of one's body on a monitor in itself does not change anything about the ways in which medical knowledge is produced. Whereas it has been claimed that medical images can contribute to dialogue and joint knowledge production between patients and medical professionals (cf. Shohat 1998), my analysis of clinical practices of real-time medical imaging mitigates such claims. Although real-time images may even seem a more likely basis for dialogue than other medical images, because of the real-time co-presence of doctor, patient and images, agential distributions of seeing and reading does not guarantee a meaningful dialogue whatsoever, as I have illustrated in chapter 4.[82] A mere call for better information in order for patients to become knowledgeable spectators and participants in medical knowledge production, holds an implicit recognition of biomedical knowledge production and action over that of patients.

It is highly questionable whether the empowerment of patients should be an objective of real-time medical imaging anyway, even if patients' own knowledge and experiences would be taken seriously. The underlying premise of pleas in favor of the transformation of patients into critical consumers and citizens, is that patients are in need of (more) power, autonomy or articulation. It is a questionable premise fitting a discourse of choice that is dominant in contemporary health care as well as in many other areas of society these days. The logic of choice fits best to an interpretative frame as presented in the first column of the above table, with its emphasis on information, representation and the body as condition. Annemarie Mol has pleaded for the rehabilitation of a logic that fits the constructivist frame indicated in the second column, focusing on agency, practice and the body as a proposition. It is a logic of care that has implicitly informed the organization of western health care until

---

[82] Where I used the term 'agential cut' to describe how physicians obtain the agency to see and know, whereas patients' agency lies in feeling and experiencing.

recently (Mol 2006). These days, however, 'good care' as the primary goal of health care is more and more surpassed by 'autonomy' and 'freedom of choice'. Mol argues that for patients in need of good care, it might not be very beneficial to be addressed to as a consumer or a citizen. Patients seem to be better off when they are taken seriously as patients, i.e. as people sharing agency rather than having autonomy. From that point of view, many real-time imaging practices I observed were rather successful.

I have described how patients were actively involved in collective productions, readings and translations of medical imaging events that affected their bodies and their lives. Physicians were the ones who took responsibilities and made decisions, yet patients were actors in regaining or maintaining health or in coping with illness. Flyers and physicians should make explicit that the practice of real-time imaging is a collective effort with limited possibilities. Real-time images neither present reality nor yield objective knowledge, but produce clues that can be meaningful when combined with clues from other sources.

Reflexivity in practice

I hope that my analysis of embodied illness experience in real-time imaging practices has contributed to insights into

> locating the objective referent, understanding the epistemic and psychic seductiveness of visual representations, understanding the epistemological and ontological consequences of making particular virtual cuts, and getting practitioners (*and patients, MR*) to reflect on the ways in which (...) technology has the potential to both erase and initiate the patient's subjectivity. (Barad 1998: 119)

Rather than in straightforward applications or recommendations, the practical value of empirical-philosophical analysis lies in the promotion of reflexive medical practices.[83] Promoting reflexivity is a way to improve the quality of care (cf. Mesman 2002: 149-60; Pols 2004: 155). My book provides input for contemplations and discussions between and among health care professionals, managers, patients and policy makers by evoking questions like: What do we do when we make and watch images? What do images *do* in the production of knowledge and experience? Which unintended consequences may real-time imaging have?

---

[83] Although the previous contemplations may seem a mere footnote to my analysis, I judge it necessary to prevent any easy translation of it into such straightforward recommendations and applications. As tempting as it may be, it risks violating the sophistication of this kind of work.

How can watching contribute to coping with uncertainty, with a sick body, with a disturbed life? How do we live with technological images of our bodies?

An academic thesis, however, is not an appropriate medium to reach physicians and patients and promote reflexive practices. Doing fieldwork is. My presence during examinations and in the departments made some patients and physicians 'see things differently'. Translations of my analysis for biomedical and patient's audiences in professional and popular publications and presentations will be necessary to extend that effect. In this book I have only been able to explore empirical and theoretical grounds for a notion of illness experience as a result of distributed embodiment. It enables a description of how medicine and medical technologies add to lived embodiment rather than reduce it or subtract from it. That opens up possibilities for critical yet constructive interventions in medical practices as well as in cultural practices where images of medicine and technology are produced. In the scope of this project I have not engaged in such theoretically informed and informative contributions to the quality of care and decision making in the actual practices of study, yet I hope that my findings and conclusions will find their way into interventionist projects by myself and others.

As I said before, at present there seems to be little reason to instigate reflection and discussion about real-time medical imaging. Neither patients nor physicians report substantial problems in clinical imaging practices. Of course, things go wrong sometimes, but they usually do not cost lives or cause tremendous suffering. Most real-time imaging events seem to exemplify 'good care' where agency is shared between patients' bodies, technical devices and medical professionals. Moreover, real-time medical imaging technologies – being relatively cheap – are not an obvious target for critiques on capital-intensive health care. The uncontested status of real-time imaging is what made it a good case for my (theoretical) objective to analyze techno-visual mediations of embodied illness experience. However, real-time imaging is not the best case for testing any claims on the ramifications of my conceptual work for the improvement of care practices.

My analysis may contribute to the assessment of other imaging practices that pose more ground for debate among physicians, patients or other social groups. The raising popularity of 'complete body scans', offering people the possibility to check their condition through various imaging and other medical technologies, is an example. Commercial providers of such tests build on people's trust in the objectivity of medical technologies. Policy makers and insurance companies have doubts about prohibiting or reimbursing the examinations, and patients consider the costs and benefits. My analysis of medical imaging might provide a broader perspective for their considerations. Another fascinating case is presented by recent neuropsychological research about the possibilities for real-time functional MRI representations of brain activity in neurofeedback therapy (Weiskopf et al. 2004). Those and other projects and initiatives attract a lot of media attention and contribute to the distribution of the myth of a transparent body and accompanying high expectations. Therefore they are prone to criticisms presenting such developments as yet another instance of undesirable medical alienation. Those are just as one-sided as the transparency trope. The analysis in this book has provided ingredients for a more nuanced and sensible debate about how (real-time) visual presentations affect human bodies on the outside and on the inside.

References

Akrich, M. (1992) The de-scription of technical objects. In W. Bijker and J. Law (eds.) *Shaping technology, building society: studies in sociotechnical change*. Cambridge: MIT Press, 205-224.

Akrich, M. and B. Pasveer (2004) Embodiment and disembodiment in childbirth narratives. *Body and Society* 10 (2-3): 63-84.

Barad, K. (1996) Meeting the universe halfway: realism and social constructivism without contradiction. In: Hankinson Nelson, L and J. Nelson (eds) *Feminism, science, and the philosophy of science*. Dordrecht: Kluwer Press, 161-94.

----------. (1998) Getting real: technoscientific practices and the materialization of reality. *Differences: A journal of feminist cultural studies* 10 (2): 87-126.

Barker, K.K. (1998) A ship upon a stormy sea: the medicalization of pregnancy. *Social Science and Medicine* 47 (8): 1067-76.

Baszanger, I. (1998) *Inventing pain medicine: from the laboratory to the clinic*. New Jersey: Rutgers University Press.

Beaulieu, A. (2002) Images are not the (only) truth: brain mapping, visual knowledge, and iconoclasm. *Science, Technologies and Human Values* 27 (1): 53-86.

Berg, M. and M. Akrich (2004) Introduction – Bodies on trial: performances and politics in medicine and biology. *Body and Society* 10 (2-3): 1-12.

Berg, M. and G. Bowker (1997) The multiple bodies of the medical record: towards a sociology of an artifact. *The Sociological Quarterly* 38 (3): 511-535.

Blume, S. (1992) *Insight and industry : on the dynamics of technological change in medicine*. Cambridge: MIT Press.

Bowker, G. (1994) *Science on the run: information management and industrial geophysics at Schlumberger, 1920-1940*. Cambridge: MIT Press.

Bruner, E.M. (1986) Experience and its expressions. In: Turner, V.W. & E.M. Bruner (eds) *The anthropology of experience*. Urbana and Chicago: University of Illinois Press.

Burri, R. (2001) Doing images: zur soziotechnischen Fabrikation visueller Erkenntnisin der Medizin. In: Heintz, B. & J. Huber (eds) *Mit dem Auge denken. Strategien der Sichtbarmachung in wissenschaftlichen und virtuellen Welten*. Zürich/Wien: Springer Verlag, 277-304.

Butler, J. (1993) *Bodies that matter: on the discursive limits of 'sex'*. London: Routledge.

Callon, M. (1986) Some elements of a sociology of translation: domestication of the scallops and the fishermen of Saint Brieuc Bay. In J. Law (ed.) *Power, action and belief: a new sociology of knowledge?* London: Routledge and Kegan Paul, 196-233.

Callon, M. and V. Rabeharisoa (n.d.) Articulating bodies: the case of muscular dystrophies, http://www.tik.uio.no/Callon_and_Rabeharisoa.pdf.

Cartwright, L. (1995) *Screening the body: tracing medicine's visual culture*. Minneapolis: University of Minnesota Press.

Csordas, T.J. (1990) Embodiment as a paradigm for anthropology. *Ethos* 18 (1): 5-47.

---------------. (1994) *Embodiment and experience: the existential ground of culture and self*. Cambridge: Cambridge University Press.

Cussins, C. (1998) Ontological choreography: agency for women patients in an infertility clinic. In: Berg, M. & A. Mol (eds.), *Differences in Medicine. Unraveling practices, techniques, and bodies*. Durham & London: Duke University Press.

Desjarlais, R. (1996) Struggling along. In: Jackson, M. (ed.) *Things as they are. New directions in phenomenological anthropology*. Bloomington: Indiana University Press, 70-93.

Dijck, J. v. (2001) Bodies without borders: the endoscopic gaze. *International Journal for Cultural Studies* 4 (2): 219-37.

Dijck, J. v. (2005) *The transparent body. A cultural analysis of medical imaging.* Seattle: University of Washington Press.

Duden, B. (1993a) Visualizing 'Life'. *Science as Culture* 3 (4), 17: 562-99.

------------ (1993b) *Disembodying women: perspectives on pregnancy and the unborn.* Cambridge: Harvard University Press.

Dumit, J. (1997) A digital image of the category of the person: PET scanning and objective self-fashioning. In: Downey, G.L. and J. Dumit (eds) *Cyborgs and citadels: anthropological interventions in emerging sciences and technologies.* Santa Fe: School of American Research Press, 83-102.

----------.(2004) *Picturing personhood. Brain scans and biomedical identity.* Princeton: Princeton University Press.

Eisenberg, L. (1977) The search for care. *Daedalus* 106: 235-46.

Engelshoven, J. v. (2002) Medical images in practice: radiologists' questions. Presentation for symposium Biomedical imaging meets computer vision, Technical University Eindhoven, March 22, 2002.

Fabian, J. (1991) Presence and representation. In: Fabian, J. *Time and the work of anthropology. Critical essays 1971-1991.* Chur: Harwood Academic Publishers, 207-223.

Franklin, S. (1997) *Embodied progress: a cultural account of assisted conception.* London: Routledge.

Foucault, M. (1972) *Archaelogy of knowledge.* London: Tavistock Publications, originally published in French in 1969.

--------------. (1973) *The birth of the clinic: an archaeology of medical perception.* London: Tavistock Publications, originally published in French in 1963.

Ginkel, R. v. (1998) The repatriation of anthropology: some observations on endo-ethnography. *Anthropology and Medicine* 5 (3): 251-68.

Gomart, E. and A. Hennion (1999), A sociology of attachment: music amateurs, drug users. In: Law J. & J. Hassard (eds) *Actor Network Theory and after.* Oxford: Blackwell, 220-247.

Good, B.J. (1994) *Medicine, rationality and experience: an anthropological perspective.* Cambridge: Cambridge University Press.

Grosz, E.A. (1994) *Volatile bodies: toward a corporeal feminism.* Bloomington: Indiana University Press.

Gumbrecht, H.U. (1998) Perception versus experience: moving pictures and their resistance to interpretation. In: Lenoir, T. (ed) *Inscribing science: scientific texts and the materiality of communication.* Stanford: Stanford University Press.

--------------------. (2004) *Productions of presence. What meaning cannot convey.* Stanford: Stanford University Press.

Hansen, M. (2000) *Embodying technesis: technology beyond writing.* Ann Arbor: University of Michigan Press.

Haraway, D. (1988) Situated knowledges: the science question in feminism and the privilege of partial perspective. *Feminist Studies* (14) (3): 575-99.

--------------. (1991) *Simians, cyborgs and women: the reinvention of nature.* London: Free Association Books.

Hayles, N.K. (2000) Foreword: clearing the ground. In: Hansen, M. *Embodying technesis: technology beyond writing.* Ann Arbor: University of Michigan Press.

Helman, C.G (2001) *Culture, health and illness.* Fourth edition (first edition 1984). London: Arnold.

Heidegger, M. (1962) *Being and time.* New York: Harper & Row, originally published in German in 1927.

Hennepe, M. te (2007) Depicting skin: visual culture in nineteenth-century medicine. Maastricht University: PhD thesis.

Hirschauer, S. (1991) The manufacture of bodies in surgery. *Social Studies of Science* 21 (2): 279-319.

Holtzmann-Kevles, B. (1997) *Naked to the bone: medical imaging in the twentieth century.* New Brunswick: Rutgers University Press.

Houwaart, E.S. and S. Kruisinga (2001) De echografie in Nederland: de eerste vijftien jaar. In: Schot, J.W. et al. (eds) *Techniek in Nederland in de twintigste eeuw. Deel IV: Huishouden. Medische techniek.* Zutphen: Walburg Pers, 251-71.

Hydén, L.-C. (1997) Illness and narratives. *Sociology of health and illness* 19 (1): 48-69.

Ihde, D. (1990) *Technology and the lifeworld: from garden to earth.* Bloomington: Indiana University Press.

--------. (2002) *Bodies in technology.* Minneapolis: University of Minnesota Press.

--------. (2003) Postphenomenology – again. Working paper no. 3. Aarhus: Centre for STS studies., Department of Information & Media Studies, University of Aarhus.

Jackson, M. (ed.) (1996) *Things as they are: new directions in phenomenological anthropology.* Bloomington: Indiana University Press.

Kleinman, A. (1980) *Patients and healers in the context of culture.* Berkeley: University of California Press.

---------------. (1988) *The illness narratives. Suffering, healing, and the human condition.* New York: Basic Books.

Kleinman, A. and J. Kleinman (1998) Suffering and its professional transformation: toward an ethnography of interpersonal experience. In: Geest, S. v.d. and A. Rienks (eds) *The art of medical anthropology*, Amsterdam: Het Spinhuis: 199-214. Reprinted with abridgements from *Culture, medicine and psychiatry* 15 (3): 275-301, 1991.

Lacan, J. (1953) Some reflections on the Ego. *The International Journal of Psychoanalysis* 34: 11-19.

Lajer-Burcharth, E. (1997) Real bodies: video in the 1990s. *Art History* 20 (2): 185-213.

Lammer, C. (2002) *Patient* bodies. The fabrication of moving body landscapes in angiograhy and interventional radiology. *Medische Antropologie* 14 (1): 90-107.

Latour, B. (1987) *Science in action: how to follow scientists and engineers through society.* Cambridge.: Harvard University Press.

----------. (1990) Drawing things together. In: Lynch, M. and S. Woolgar (eds.), *Representation in scientific practice.* Cambridge, MA: MIT Press, 19-68.

----------. (1999a) *Pandora's hope: essays on the reality of science studies.* Cambridge, MA: Harvard University Press.

----------. (1999b) On recalling ANT. In: In: Law J. and J. Hassard (eds) *Actor Network Theory and after.* Oxford: Blackwell, 15-25.

----------. (2004) How to talk about the body? The normative dimension of science studies. *Body and Society* 10 (2-3): 205-229.

----------. (2005) *Re-assembling the social: an introduction to actor-network-theory.* Oxford: Oxford University Press.

Law, J. (1992) Notes on the theory of the actor-network: ordering, strategy and heterogeneity. *Systems Practice* 5: 379-393.

-------. After ANT: topology, naming and complexity. In: Law J. and J. Hassard (eds) *Actor Network Theory and after.* Oxford: Blackwell, 1-14.

Leder, D. (1990) *The absent body.* Chicago: The University of Chicago Press.

Lupton, D. (2003) *Medicine as culture: illness, disease and medicine in Western societies.* Second edition (first edition published in 1994). London: SAGE.

Martin, E. (1987) *The woman in the body: a cultural analysis of reproduction.* Boston: Beacon Press.

----------. (1994) *Flexible bodies: tracking immunity in American culture - from the days of polio to the age of AIDS.* Boston: Beacon Press.

Mattingly, C. and L.C. Garro (eds) (2000) *Narrative and the cultural construction of illness and healing.* Berkeley and Los Angeles: University of California Press.

Merleau-Ponty, M. (1945) *Phénomenologie de la perception.* Paris : Gallimard.

Mesman, J. (2002) *Ervaren pioniers : omgaan met twijfel in de intensive care voor pasgeborenen.* Amsterdam: Uitgeverij Aksant.

Mitchell, L.M. (2001) *Baby's first picture: ultrasound and the politics of fetal subjects.* Toronto: University of Toronto Press.

Mol, A. (1998) Missing links, making links: the performance of some atheroscleroses. In: Berg, M. and A. Mol (eds) *Differences in medicine. Unraveling practices, techniques, and bodies.* Durham: Duke University Press, 144-65.

-------. (2001) Meer technologie, meer praten. In: Mol, A. and M. Berg (eds) *Ingebouwde normen. Medische technieken doorgelicht.* Utrecht: Van der Wees Uitgeverij.

-------. (2002) *The body multiple: ontology in medical practice.* Durham: Duke University Press.

-------. (2006) *De logica van het zorgen. Actieve patiënten en de grenzen van het kiezen.* Amsterdam: Uitgeverij Van Gennep.

Mol, A. and M. Berg (1998) Differences in medicine: an introduction. In: Berg, M. & A. Mol (eds) *Differences in medicine. Unraveling practices, techniques, and bodies.* Durham: Duke University Press, 1-12.

Mol, A. and J. Law (2004) Embodied action, enacted bodies: the example of hypoglycaemia. *Body and Society* 10 (2-3): 43-62.

Mueller-Rockstroh, B. (2007) Ultrasound travels. The politics of a medical technology in Ghana and Tanzania. Maastricht University: PhD thesis.

Novas, C. and N. Rose (2000) Genetic risk and the birth of the somatic individual. *Economy and Society* 29 (4): 485-513.

Oudkerk, M. (2002) Vervreemding van het menselijk lichaam (De imago corporis humani). Inaugural speech delivered November 5th 2002, University of Groningen.

Pasveer, B. (1989) Knowledge of shadows – the introduction of X-ray images in medicine. *Sociology of Health and Illness* 11 (4): 361-81.

----------. (1992) Shadows of Knowledge. Making a representing practice in medicine: X-ray pictures and pulmonary tuberculosis, 1895-1930. University of Amsterdam: Ph.D. dissertation.

Pasveer, B. (1994) De coproduktie van afbeelding en ziekte: Röntgenfoto's en longtuberculose aan het begin van de twintigste eeuw. In: Geest, S. v.d., P. ten Have, G. Nijhof and P. Verbeek-Heida (eds) *De macht der dingen. Medische technologie in cultureel perspectief.* Amsterdam: Het Spinhuis, 20-43.

Persson, A., K. Race and E. Wakeford (2003) HIV health in context: negotiating medical technology and lived experience. *Health* 7 (4): 397-415.

Petchesky, R. (1987) Foetal images: the power of visual culture in the politics of reproduction. In: Stanworth, M. (ed.) *Reproductive technologies: gender, motherhood and medicine.* Cambridge: Polity Press, 57-80.

Pols, A.J. (2004) *Good care: enacting a complex ideal in long-term psychiatry.* Utrecht: Trimbosinstituut.

Pool, R. (1994) *Dialogue and the interpretation of illness: conversations in a Cameroon village.* Oxford: Berg.

Prasad, A. (2005) Making images/ making bodies: visibilizing and disciplining through Magnetic Resonance Imaging (MRI). *Science, Technology and Human Values* 30 (2): 291-316.

Prentice, R. (2005) The anatomy of a surgical simulation: the mutual articulation of bodies in and through the machine. *Social Studies of Science* 35 (6): 837-66.

Price, F. (1996) Now you see it, now you don't: mediating science and managing uncertainty in reproductive medicine. In: Irwin, A. and B. Wynne (eds) *Misunderstanding science? The public reconstruction of science and technology.* Cambridge: Cambridge University Press, 84-106.

Radstake, M. (2000) *Secrecy and ambiguity: home-based care for people living with HIV/AIDS in Ghana.* Leiden: African Studies Centre.

Rapp, R. (1997) Real-time fetus. The role of the sonogram in the age of monitored reproduction. In: Downey, G.L. and J. Dumit (eds) *Cyborgs and citadels.. Anthropological interventions in emerging sciences and technologies.* Santa Fe: School of American Research Press, 31-48.

Rogers, M.F. (1983) *Sociology, ethnomethodology, and experience: a phenomenological critique.* Cambridge: Cambridge University Press.

Saunders, B. (forthcoming) *CT Suite: the work of diagnosis in the age of noninvasive cutting.* Durham: Duke University Press.

Sawchuk, K. (2000) Biotourism, Fantastic Voyage, and sublime inner space. In: J. Marchessault and K. Sawchuk (eds), *Wild science. Reading feminism, medicine and the media.* London and New York: Routledge, 9-23.

Scheper-Hughes, N. and M. Lock (1998) The mindful body. A prolegomenon to future work in medical anthropology. In: Geest, S. v.d. and A. Rienks (eds) *The art of medical anthropology,* Amsterdam: Het Spinhuis. Reprinted with minor abridgements from *Medical Anthropology Quarterly* 1 (1): 6-41, 1987.

Shohat, E. (1998) "Lasers for ladies". Endo discourse and the inscription of science. In: Treichler, P., L. Cartwright and C. Penley (eds) *The visible woman: imaging technologies, gender and science.* New York: New York University Press, 240-70.

Smeenk, A.D.J. and H.A.M.J. ten Have (2003) Medicalization and obstetric care: An analysis of developments in Dutch midwifery. *Medicine, health care and philosophy* 6 (2): 153-65.

Sobchack, V. (2004) *Carnal thoughts: embodiment and moving image culture.* Berkeley: University of California Press.

Sontag, S. (1991) *Illness as metaphor and AIDS and its metaphors.* London: Penguin Books.

Stabile, C.A. (1998) Shooting the mother: fetal photography and the politics of disappearance. In: Treichler, P., L. Cartwright and C. Penley (eds) *The visible woman: imaging technologies, gender and science.* New York: New York University Press, 171-197.

Stacey, J. (1998) *Teratologies: a cultural analysis of cancer.* London: Routledge.

Sturken, M. and L. Cartwright (2001) *Practices of looking - an introduction to visual culture.* Oxford: Oxford University Press.

Taylor, J.S. (1998) Image of contradiction: obstetrical ultrasound in American culture. In: Franklin, S. and H. Ragoné (eds) *Reproducing reproduction. Kinship, power, and technological innovation.* Philadelphia: University of Pennsylvania Press, 15-45.

The, A.M. , T. Hak, G. Köeter & G. v.d. Wal (2003) Radiographic images and the emergence of optimism about recovery in patients with small call lung cancer: an ethnographic study. *Lung Cancer* 41 (1): 113-20.

Timmerman, S. and M. Berg (2003) *The gold standard: the challenge of evidence-based medicine and standardization in health care.* Philadelphia: Temple University Press.

Toombs, S.K. (1992) *The meaning of illness. A phenomenological account of the different perspectives of physician and patient.* Dordrecht: Kluwer Academic Publishers.

Turner, B. (1992) *Regulating bodies: essays in medical sociology.* London: Routledge.

Varela, F.J. (2001) Intimate distances. Fragments for a phenomenology of organ transplantation. *Journal of Consciousness Studies* 8 (5-7): 259-71.

Verbeek, P.-P. (2005a) *What things do. Philosophical reflections on technology, agency, and design.* University Park, Pennsylvania: Pennsylvania State University Press.

Verbeek, P.-P. (2005b) Artifacts and attachment – a post-script philosophy of mediation. In: Harbers, H. (ed.) *Inside the politics of technology. Agency and normativity in the co-production of technology and society.* Amsterdam: Amsterdam University Press, 125-46.

---------------. (2006) Materializing morality – design ethics and technological mediation. *Science, Technology and Human Values* 31(3): 361-380.

Weiskopf, N., K. Mathiak, S.W. Bock, F. Scharnowski, R. Veit, W. Grodd, R. Goebel and N. Birbaumer (2004) Principles of a brain-computer interface (BCI) based on real-time functional magnetic resonance imaging (fMRI). *IEEE Transactions on Biomedical Engineering* 51 (6): 966-970.

Weiss, G. (1999) *Body images. Embodiment as intercorporeality.* New York: Routledge.

Willems, D. L. (1995) Tools of care: explorations into the semiotics of medical technology. Maastricht: Rijksuniversiteit Limburg, PhD thesis.

Williams, S.J. and G. Bendelow (1998) *The lived body: sociological themes, embodied issues.* London: Routledge.

Young, K. (1989) Disembodiment: the phenomenology of the body in medical examinations. *Semiotica* 73 (1/2): 43-66.

------------. (1997) *Presence in the flesh. The body in medicine.* Cambridge, MA: Harvard University Press.

Yoxen, E. (1987) Seeing with sound: A study of the development of medical images. In: Bijker, W., T. Hughes and T. Pinch (eds) *The social construction of technological systems: new directions in the sociology and history of technology.* Cambridge, MA: MIT Press.

Visions of illness. An endography of real-time medical imaging

English summary

Medical imaging is among the core activities of contemporary biomedicine. Ultrasound, fluoroscopy and endoscopy are *real-time* medical imaging technologies that produce 'live' moving pictures of the interior body, which patients can often watch during the examination. In this book I show *how real-time medical imaging affects patients' embodied experience of illness*.

Medical images are not mere representations of given bodies: they *mediate* human embodiment. Real-time images refer to a body that is the object of medical examination by a physician as well as the object *and* the subject of a patient's sensory perception and agency. In this book I describe the transformations of bodies and images in various stages of imaging grounded on fieldwork in the radiology and endoscopy departments of a Dutch hospital. For that purpose I develop a method and vocabulary to describe the production of embodied experiences of health and illness related to such transformations.

In *chapter 2* I explore conceptual frames from the interpretative anthropology and sociology of health and medicine, from phenomenology, from actor-network theory (ANT), and from post-phenomenology in order to collect building blocks for that vocabulary. I introduce three core concepts successively: *illness* from medical anthropology, *embodied experience* from phenomenology, and *technological mediation* from actor-network theory and post-phenomenology.

Medical anthropologists use the word *illness* to denote an individual's psychosocial and cultural experience of being ill. They use the notion of *disease* to refer to physical or mental abnormalities in the structure and functions of a body, which are the object of professional medicine. Technology is commonly associated with the medical professional outlook on (ill-) health and therefore said to widen the gap between disease and illness. The distinction between disease as the object of medical knowledge and illness as the object of lay experience is at odds with a study of illness as an embodied experience, for it implies a distinction between the patient as person (being ill) and as body (having a disease). A narrative bias, a poor vocabulary to describe material aspects of experience, an instrumental definition of technology, and the illness/disease dualism are the main shortcomings of an interpretative social-scientific framework for my purpose.

For *phenomenologists* embodiment is the basis of all human experience. Medical imaging technologies transform *body images*, which are part of *embodied experience*. Phenomenologists have been concerned with the mediating role of technologies, yet rarely been with illness experience. Furthermore phenomenologists consider to be alienating. Since I want to know how technology shapes one's own body, I look for a more appropriate way to describe the work of technology.

Actor-network theory (ANT) describes the identities of humans and things not as given, but as resulting from the relations between entities. Technologies mediate such relations. With ANT's material semiotics I can describe technological mediations of agency, yet I cannot address how *experience* is technologically mediated. *Post-phenomenology* attempts to join the best of two worlds: a phenomenological concept of experience, and ANT's notion of *technological mediation*. The strength of post-phenomenology is its analysis of the role of instruments in making the world present for people and in making people act in the world. My question about technological mediation of bodies as subject and as object of (illness) experience, addresses the relations between what Don Ihde has called 'here-bodies' and 'image-bodies'. The 'here-body' is the embodied subject that moves, perceives, senses and is-in-the- world. The 'image-body' is one's own body as an object of perception. An analysis of either here-bodies or image-bodies misses a crucial quality of embodied experience: that experience is enacted in relations between bodies and images.

The subsequent chapters present empirical material showing that the specific impact of real-time medical imaging on illness experience cannot properly be described in terms of either medical anthropology, (post-)phenomenology or actor-network theory. That specificity especially relates to the *visual* nature of the technology's impact, the fact that it concerns *interior* bodies, and the possibility for *patients* to watch images in *real-time*, simultaneously with the physician who produces them. The third, fourth and fifth chapters present the subsequent stages of preparation of bodies for imaging, image production, and translation of images in knowledge and experience.

In *chapter 3* I describe what happens to patients' bodies before they end up on an examination table and on a monitor. Imaging devices, physicians, protocols and patients themselves prepare bodies for real-time imaging. Before there has been any physical contact between a patient and an imaging device, particular features and abilities are already inscribed in the design, set-up and intended use of the technology, ranging from interior dynamics and exterior transparency to the possibility of active cooperation and spectatorship. Besides the imaging device, the training of physicians, technicians and nurses also affects the body that will be the object of real-time imaging. The coordination of visual and haptic skills is characteristic for the performance of ultrasound, fluoroscopy and endoscopy. Prospective imaging professionals also learn that real-time imaging produces data that are relatively subjective. Whereas X-ray, CT and MRI produces objective images, which are readable to everyone who has acquired a professional radiological gaze, real-time images are only meaningful to those who actually made them.

Many examinations require patients to adjust their diet and purge their intestines. By meeting such requirements, patients actively prepare their body for its role as object of medical examination. The information on the procedure, which they receive from physicians and by other means, also contributes to the formation of a frame for patients' experiences of real-time imaging. Most information flyers, for example, present one's body as an object of examination that one can actively prepare, yet do not mention that patients will be able to watch the monitor during a real-time imaging event. Forms and protocols present a fourth category of actors involved in the preparation of patients' bodies. I discuss the role of request forms especially, which categorize, reduce and multiply bodies into various objects, coordinating the actions by machines, physicians and patients. The request for a particular kind of examination and the specific phrasing of the question aims at translating what is felt in something that can be seen.

The preparations for real-time imaging by imaging devices, professionals, patients and forms constitute a process of *collective embodiment*, setting the conditions for the eventual visual transformation of patients' bodies into potential seats of disease/illness. From the very moment that a patient's experiencing and experienced body meets the objectified medical image of a body, the development of both modes of embodiment is interconnected and the medical anthropological distinction between illness and disease looses its descriptive and analytical power.

In *chapter 4* I describe the translation of bodies into real-time images as a particular production of bodily *presence*. In two respects real-time imaging is distinct from other ways of medical representation: the evanescence of the images and the presence of the patient during image-production. The patients watches how real-time images appear instantly upon acquisition. Real-time imaging leaves few material traces, like stored stills or prints.

To describe the impact of those particular characteristics on embodied experience, I distinguish four modes of attachment, viz. ways in which patients' bodies and real-time images are connected during real-time imaging events. The *first* mode of attachment originates from the real-time interpretation of images by medical professionals. Bodies and images are connected in physician's real-time readings and in the communication between doctor and patient during an examination. To physicians, images are semi-finished data sets that need to be molded into information, which can be represented visually, numerically or otherwise. Doctors' real-time readings inform patients' perceptions of their own body. The *second* mode of attachment comes into being in the confrontation of patients' visual perceptions of images of their own interior body and their simultaneous sensory perceptions of the imaging procedure. It enables patients to identify with the images on the monitor. The *third* mode of attachment results from the simultaneous passivity and activity of patients' bodies in a network of distributed agency. The *fourth* mode of attachment consists in patients' emotional responses to the images and the imaging procedure, like fear or embarrassment.

During a real-time imaging event, the patient's body is simultaneously present in various qualities: as the body that a patient sees, feels and acts with; as the body on the examination table that is the object of medical examination; and as the body on the monitor represented by black and white shapes or colorful structures. The real-time connection between the different bodily qualities constitutes a *production of presence* that resembles the experience of watching oneself in a mirror. Seeing oneself acting at the very moment of the act, establishes a direct link between the body in the mirror (or on the monitor) and the person in front of it (or on the examination table).

The analysis of modes of attachment and productions of presence shows once more how real-time imaging technologies mediate bodies as 'objects' as well as 'subjects' of perception, knowledge and experience – of disease and of illness. Analyzing material-discursive attachments of patients' bodies and real-time images actually offers a way out of such dualisms, which hamper an understanding of embodied experience as technologically mediated.

In *chapter 5* I describe how images, perceptions, interpretations and experiences during a real-time imaging event, are translated into diagnoses by professionals and into narratives and body images by patients. Both translation trajectories contribute to the enactment of embodied experiences of health and illness. Once the real-time imaging event is over, the co-presence of the patient's body on the examination table and on the monitor is disconnected. An examination does not simply produce a diagnosis, nor a coherent narrative or body image. Real-time images only require durable referents in two connected trajectories of translation: the professional translation of imaging results into examination reports that contribute to a medical diagnosis; and the primarily narrative translation into a patient's experience. Imaging reports seem very different from patients' narratives. However, they both bear the marks of their joint origin in the preparations of a body for real-time imaging – described in chapter 3 – and in the production of real-time images, described in chapter 4. In the examination report imaging physicians compose findings from a variety of visual and other data. Those findings are further translated into diagnoses by attending physicians. Patients witness two moments in the professional translation trajectory: the translation during the examination by the image producer, and afterwards the translation by their attending physician who communicates the results of the examination. Patients include and transform professional practices of reading and writing in their translations of imaging events in their primarily narrative expressions of experience.

The comparison of real-time images to mirrors in chapter 4 suggested a constitutive role for real-time imaging in the formation of *body images*. However, technological mediation concerns not so much body images but *image-bodies*, which are the objects of experience constitutive for patients' illness experiences. Four related categories of image-bodies emerge as referents for real-time imaging events: the *medical body* that is constructed in professional translations; the *transparent body* that results from converging medical and media technologies; the *spectacular body* that the patient has watched on the monitor; and the *lived body* that is actively engaged in the imaging event as an embodied spectator and actor.

The confrontations of image-bodies may result in disembodiment and alienated experiences of illness, but may also evoke patients' identification with images. The construction of a particular experience hinges on the (in)compatibility of physicians' and patients' translations. I suggest substituting the notion of 'mediation' by that of Bruno Latour's idea of 'a body learning to be affected', since it better covers the overtone of interconnected interferences of real-time imaging with embodied experience. Real-time images are not reflections of a body's condition nor do they automatically alienating bodies from selves: through real-time imaging bodies learn to be affected.

The diffuse and contradictory experiences of patients taking part in real-time imaging events require a concept of illness that acknowledges and addresses the hermeneutic as well as the material and existential layers of embodiment. In the final phase of image translation as it is described in chapter 5, illness cannot be detached from the medical-professional objectivation of a body's condition any more than in the phases of preparation and image-production described in the previous chapters. When described separately, the production of medical knowledge can easily be contrasted to the enactment of illness: one trajectory involves the translation of images into written language, via a reading of images as data-sets; in the other trajectory, images are rather read as pictures and translated into narrative expressions of experience. Presenting the trajectories as being in line rather than parallel, however, affords a description of the co-production of medical knowledge and embodied experience that results in illness as a technologically mediated, layered experience. An analysis of techno-visual mediation of embodied experience needs an extended (ANT) description of the networks from which bodies emerge and in which illness circulates as the referent of medical images, as well as a detailed (phenomenological) account of how people experience those bodies.

My analysis of real-time medical imaging challenges two tropes commonly presented as opposites in the public domain and in social-scientific discourse: the trope of the transparent body, accessed and controlled by medical technology; and the trope of alienation, with medical technologies objectifying and disembodying patients. Many physicians consider patients' high expectations of medical imaging to be unrealistic. I argue that medical practices themselves produce such high expectations. Physicians contribute to the cultural discourse of a 'transparent body' when they present real-time imaging in terms of 'seeing what is wrong'. The apparently self-evident possibility for patients to watch the monitor is part of that practice. Not meeting patients' expectations may indeed result in alienation. To prevent that, physicians need to understand that watching images of their own interior is a complicated experience for many patients.

My analysis can prevent misunderstandings by making that complicated experience understandable. A different notion of real-time medical imaging by patients as well as by physicians can prevent misunderstandings and affords an understanding of that complicated experience. In various stages of translation, the body and the phenomenon 'illness' obtain multiple hermeneutic, material and existential layers. Rather than the outcome of processes of signification, or an inherent quality of bodies, illness is a matter of practice. Using medical anthropology to describe expressions of experience, actor-network theory to trace conditions for experience, and post-phenomenology to understand technological mediation of experience, I have developed a vocabulary for the analysis of that multilayered experience as a mode of *distributed embodiment*.

For patients, what they see, hear and feel during a real-time imaging trajectory is often confusing and inconsistent. A notion like 'distributed embodiment' presents a conceptual strategy to deal with that inconsistence. It could be translated into practice by including in hospital flyers information to prepare patients for what the monitor will show during an examination. However, that implies that patients' knowledge should be better aligned with biomedical knowledge, in order to obtain a kind of 'informed agency'. That is not what I intend to suggest. Enhancing patients' power and autonomy by providing information fits a discourse of choice that is dominant these days in contemporary health care as well as in many other areas of society. A constructivist approach as I have presented, however, rather fits a logic of care. Patients benefit from being taken serious as patients, i.e. as people sharing agency rather than having autonomy. What flyers and physicians should do is make explicit that real-time imaging is a collective effort with limited possibilities, not presenting reality or yielding objective knowledge, but producing clues that can result in a diagnosis when combined with clues from other sources. That requires reflexive medical practices, to which I hope to contribute with this book.

Ziektebeelden. Een endografie van real-time medische visualisering

Nederlandse samenvatting

Medische beeldvorming behoort tot de kernactiviteiten van de moderne geneeskunde. Echoscopie, doorlichting en endoscopie zijn *real-time* beeldvormingstechnieken die 'live' bewegende beelden van de binnenkant van het eigen lichaam produceren, die patiënten vaak tijdens het onderzoek zelf kunnen zien. In dit boek laat ik zien hoe real-time medische beeldvorming de belichaamde ziekte-ervaring van patiënten maakt en raakt.

Medische beelden zijn niet zomaar afbeeldingen van gegeven lichamen: ze *bemiddelen* de menselijke lichamelijkheid. Bij real-time beeldvorming is een lichaam zowel het object van medisch onderzoek door een arts, als ook het object *en* het subject van de zintuiglijke waarneming en het handelingsvermogen van een patiënt zelf. In dit boek beschrijf ik de transformaties van lichamen en van beelden in verschillende stadia van beeldvorming op basis van veldwerk op de radiologie- en endoscopieafdelingen van een Nederlands ziekenhuis. Daartoe ontwikkel ik een methode en een vocabulaire om de productie van belichaamde ervaringen van gezondheid en ziekte te beschrijven, die met zulke transformaties samenhangt.

In *hoofdstuk 2* onderzoek ik conceptuele kaders uit de interpretatieve medische antropologie en sociologie, uit de fenomenologie, uit actor-netwerk theorie (ANT) en uit de postfenomenologie om bouwstenen te verzamelen voor dat vocabulaire. Achtereenvolgens introduceer ik drie kernconcepten: *ziekte* (illness) uit de medische antropologie, *belichaamde ervaring* uit de fenomenologie en *technologische mediatie* uit actor-netwerk theorie en postfenomenologie.

Medisch antropologen gebruiken het begrip 'illness' om de individuele psychosociale en culturele ervaring van ziek-zijn aan te duiden. Hun begrip 'disease' verwijst naar lichamelijke of geestelijke afwijkingen in de structuur en functies van een lichaam, die het object zijn van professioneel medische handelen. Technologie wordt gewoonlijk geassocieerd met de medisch-professionele kijk op het lichaam. Medische technologie zou daarom de kloof tussen 'disease' en 'illness' vergroten. Het onderscheid tussen 'disease' als object van medische kennis en 'illness' als object van lekenervaring staat op gespannen voet met een onderzoek naar ziekte als lichamelijke ervaring, omdat het de patiënt als persoon (die ziek is) onderscheidt van het lichaam (dat een ziekte heeft). Een voorkeur voor narratieve analyse, een gebrekkig vocabulaire om materiële aspecten van ervaring te beschrijven, een instrumentele definitie van technologie en het 'illness/disease' dualisme zijn de grootste tekortkomingen van een interpretatief sociaal-wetenschappelijk kader voor mijn onderzoek.

Voor *fenomenologen* is lichamelijkheid de basis van alle menselijke ervaring. Medische beeldvormingstechnieken transformeren *lichaamsbeelden*, die deel uitmaken van *belichaamde ervaring*. Fenomenologen hebben zich wel beziggehouden met de bemiddelende rol van technologieën, maar zelden met ziekte-ervaring. Verder beschouwt de fenomenologie technologie vooral als vervreemdend. Omdat ik juist geïnteresseerd ben in de vraag hoe technologie het eigen lichaam vormgeeft, ga ik op zoek naar een geschiktere manier om het werk van technologie te beschrijven.

Actor-netwerk theorie (ANT) beschrijft de identiteiten van mensen en dingen niet als gegeven, maar als het resultaat van relaties tussen entiteiten. Technologieën bemiddelen zulke relaties. Met de materiële semiotiek van ANT kan ik wel de technologische bemiddeling van handelen beschrijven, maar niet begrijpen hoe *ervaring* technologisch bemiddeld wordt. *Postfenomenologie* probeert het beste van twee werelden te verenigen: een fenomenologisch begrip van ervaring en ANT's idee van *technologische bemiddeling*. De kracht van de postfenomenologie ligt in haar analyse van de rol van instrumenten in het aanwezig maken van de wereld voor mensen en in het handelen van mensen in de wereld. Mijn vraag over de technologische bemiddeling van lichamen als subject en object van (ziekte-)ervaring, gaat over de relatie tussen wat Don Ihde 'hier-lichamen' (here-bodies) en 'beeld-lichamen' (image-bodies) heeft genoemd. Het 'hier-lichaam' is het belichaamde subject dat beweegt, waarneemt, voelt en in-de-wereld-is. Het 'beeld-lichaam' is het eigen lichaam als object van waarneming. Een analyse van enkel hier-lichamen of alleen beeld-lichamen mist een cruciaal aspect van belichaamde ervaring: dat ervaring tot stand komt in relaties tussen lichamen en beelden.

De volgende hoofdstukken gebruiken empirisch materiaal om te laten zien dat de bijzondere invloed van real-time medische beeldvorming op ziekte-ervaring niet goed beschreven kan worden vanuit louter medisch-antropologisch, (post-)fenomenologisch of actor-netwerk perspectief. Het bijzondere betreft het *visuele* karakter van de impact van de technologie, het feit dat het om afbeeldingen van de *binnenkant* van lichamen gaat, en de mogelijkheid voor *patiënten* om de beelden in *real-time* te zien, tegelijk met de arts die ze maakt. Het derde, vierde en vijfde hoofdstuk beschrijven de opeenvolgende stadia van de voorbereiding van lichamen op beeldvorming, het maken van de beelden en het vertalen van beelden in kennis en ervaring.

In *hoofdstuk 3* beschrijf ik wat er gebeurt met patiëntlichamen voordat ze terechtkomen op een onderzoekstafel en op een monitor. Beeldvormingsinstrumenten, artsen, protocollen en patiënten zelf bereiden een lichaam voor op real-time beeldvorming. Voordat er enig lichamelijk contact heeft plaatsgevonden tussen patiënt en beeldvormingsinstrument, worden bepaalde kenmerken en mogelijkheden al in het lichaam ingeprent door het ontwerp, de opstelling en het beoogde gebruik van het apparaat. Het betreft onder meer de dynamiek van de binnenkant van het lichaam, de transparantie van de buitenkant en de rol van de patiënt als actieve toeschouwer. Naast het beeldvormingsinstrument is ook de opleiding van artsen, laboranten en verpleegkundigen van invloed op het lichaam dat het object wordt van real-time beeldvorming. De coördinatie van visuele en haptische vaardigheden is kenmerkend voor echoscopie, doorlichting en endoscopie. Aspirant-beeldmakers leren ook dat real-time beeldvorming relatief subjectieve data oplevert. Terwijl röntgen, CT en MRI objectieve beelden produceren die leesbaar zijn voor iedereen met een professionele radiologische blik, hebben real-time beelden alleen betekenis voor degene die ze zelf maakt of gemaakt heeft.

Voor veel onderzoeken is het nodig dat patiënten hun dieet aanpassen en ervoor zorgen dat hun darmen leeg zijn of hun blaas juist vol. Door aan zulke vereisten te voldoen, bereiden patiënten hun lichaam actief voor op zijn rol als object van medisch onderzoek. Ook informatie over de procedure, die patiënten krijgen van hun arts of op andere manieren, draagt bij aan de vorming van een kader voor hun ervaringen van real-time beeldvorming. De meeste informatiebrochures presenteren bijvoorbeeld het lichaam als een object van onderzoek dat men actief kan voorbereiden, maar besteden geen aandacht aan het feit dat patiënten tijdens het onderzoek de beelden op een monitor kunnen zien. Formulieren en protocollen vormen een vierde categorie actoren die betrokken is bij de voorbereiding van patiëntlichamen. Ik bespreek vooral de rol van aanvraagformulieren, die lichamen categoriseren, reduceren en vermenigvuldigen in verschillende objecten en het werk van apparaten, artsen en patiënten coördineren. De aanvraag voor een bepaald soort onderzoek en de specifieke vraagstelling zijn erop gericht iets dat gevoeld wordt te vertalen in iets dat gezien kan worden.

De voorbereidingen door beeldvormingsinstrumenten, beeldmakers, patiënten en formulieren vormen een proces van *collectieve belichaming*, waarin de voorwaarden worden gesteld voor de uiteindelijke visuele transformatie van patiëntlichamen in mogelijke zetels van ziekte. Vanaf het moment dat het ervarende en ervaren lichaam van een patiënt wordt geconfronteerd met het geobjectiveerde medische lichaamsbeeld, is de ontwikkeling van beide soorten lichamen met elkaar verbonden. Het medisch-antropologische onderscheid tussen 'illness' en 'disease' verliest dan zijn beschrijvende en analytische kracht.

Hoofdstuk 4 behandelt de verplaatsing/vertaling (translation)[84] van lichamen in real-time beelden als een bijzonder soort productie van lichamelijke *aanwezigheid/tegenwoordigheid* (presence).[85] Op twee belangrijke punten onderscheidt real-time beeldvorming zich van andere manieren van medische representatie: de vluchtigheid van de beelden en de aanwezigheid van de patiënt bij het maken van de beelden. De patiënt kan real-time beelden zien verschijnen op het moment dat ze gemaakt worden. Real-time beeldvorming laat weinig tastbare sporen na, zoals opgeslagen of afgedrukte beelden.

Om de invloed van deze twee kenmerken op belichaamde ervaring te beschrijven, onderscheid ik vier *vormen van hechting*, oftewel manieren waarop patiëntlichamen en real-time beelden met elkaar verbonden zijn tijdens een onderzoek. De *eerste* vorm van hechting komt voort uit de real-time interpretatie van beelden door de professionele makers ervan. In de real-time lezing van de arts en in communicatie tussen artsen en patiënten tijdens een onderzoek worden lichamen en beelden met elkaar verbonden. Voor artsen zijn beelden halffabrikaten: datasets die nog tot visuele, numerieke of andersoortige informatie gevormd moeten worden. De real-time lezing van artsen informeert hoe patiënten hun eigen lichaam waarnemen. De *tweede* vorm van hechting ontstaat in de confrontatie van de visuele waarnemingen die patiënten hebben van het binnenste van hun eigen lichaam met hun gelijktijdige zintuiglijke waarnemingen van de beeldvormingsprocedure. Die maakt het mogelijk dat patiënten zich identificeren met de beelden op de monitor. De *derde* vorm van hechting komt voort uit de gelijktijdige passiviteit en activiteit van patiëntlichamen in een netwerk van gedistribueerd handelingsvermogen. De *vierde* vorm van hechting wordt gevormd door de emotionele reacties van patiënten op de beelden en de beeldvormingsprocedure, zoals angst of gêne.

Tijdens een beeldvormend onderzoek is het lichaam van een patiënt aanwezig in verschillende hoedanigheden: als het lichaam dat een patiënt ziet en voelt en waarmee hij of zij handelt; als het lichaam op de onderzoekstafel, dat het object is van medisch onderzoek; en als het lichaam op de monitor, dat wordt verbeeld door zwart-witte vormen of kleurrijke

---

[84] Ik gebruik het Engelse begrip 'translation' in de betekenis die Bruno Latour eraan geeft: een materiële verplaatsing die tegelijk een vertaling inhoudt (cf. Latour 1999: 311).
[85] Ik vertaal het Engelse 'presence' als 'aanwezigheid' en/of als 'tegenwoordigheid', om zowel recht te doen aan de temporele als aan de ruimtelijke connotatie van het begrip.

structuren. De real-time verbinding tussen de verschillende lichamelijke hoedanigheden vormt een *productie van aanwezigheid/tegenwoordigheid* die overeenkomsten vertoont met de ervaring van jezelf in een spiegel zien. Jezelf zien handelen op het moment van de handeling brengt een directe relatie tot stand tussen het lichaam in de spiegel (of op de monitor) en de persoon ervoor (of op de onderzoekstafel).

De analyse van de totstandkoming van hechting en aanwezigheid/tegenwoordigheid laat nogmaals zien hoe real-time beeldvormende technologieën lichamen bemiddelen als zowel 'object' als ook als 'subject' van waarneming, kennis en ervaring – van 'disease' en van 'illness'. De analyse van materieel-discursieve verbindingen tussen patiëntlichamen en real-time beelden biedt juist een alternatief voor zulke dualismen, die een begrip van technologisch bemiddelde belichaamde ervaring in de weg staan.

In *hoofdstuk 5* beschrijf ik hoe beelden, waarnemingen, interpretaties en ervaringen tijdens een onderzoek door artsen worden vertaald in diagnoses en door patiënten in verhalen en lichaamsbeelden. Beide vertalingstrajecten dragen bij aan de totstandkoming van belichaamde ervaringen van ziekte en gezondheid. Zodra het beeldvormend onderzoek voorbij is, wordt de gezamenlijke aanwezigheid van het lichaam van de patiënt op de onderzoekstafel en op de monitor, verbroken. Een onderzoek levert niet zonder meer een diagnose op, noch een coherent verhaal of lichaamsbeeld. Real-time beelden verkrijgen duurzame referenten in twee met elkaar verbonden vertalingstrajecten: de professionele vertaling van beeldvormingsresultaten in onderzoeksrapporten die bijdragen aan een medische diagnose; en de hoofdzakelijk narratieve vertaling in de ervaring van een patiënt. Onderzoeksrapporten en patiëntenverhalen lijken hemelsbreed van elkaar te verschillen. Toch dragen ze allebei de sporen van hun gezamenlijke oorsprong, die ligt in het voorbereiden van een lichaam op real-time beeldvorming – beschreven in hoofdstuk 3 – en in de productie van real-time beelden, beschreven in hoofdstuk 4. In het onderzoeksrapport componeren artsen hun bevindingen uit een veelheid aan visuele en andere data. Die bevindingen worden vervolgens door behandelend artsen in diagnoses vertaald. Patiënten zijn op twee momenten in het professionele vertalingstraject getuige: tijdens het onderzoek van de vertaling door de maker van het beeld en later tijdens een consult van de vertaling van de onderzoeksresultaten door hun behandelend arts. Patiënten nemen professionele lees- en schrijfpraktijken op in hun eigen vertalingen en transformeren ze in hun hoofdzakelijke narratieve uitingen van hun ervaring.

De vergelijking van real-time beelden met spiegels in hoofdstuk 4 suggereerde een vormende rol voor real-time beelden bij het ontstaan van *lichaamsbeelden*. Technologische bemiddeling betreft echter niet zozeer lichaamsbeelden, maar *beeld-lichamen*: het object van ervaring dat vormend is voor de ziekte-ervaringen van patiënten. Vier met elkaar verbonden soorten beeld-lichamen fungeren als referent voor beeldvormende onderzoeken: het *medische lichaam* dat wordt geconstrueerd in professionele vertalingen; het *transparante lichaam* dat het resultaat is van convergerende medische en mediatechnologieën; het *lichaam als schouwspel* dat de patiënt heeft gezien op de monitor; en het *geleefde lichaam* dat actief betrokken is bij het onderzoek als een belichaamde toeschouwer en actor.

De confrontatie van beeld-lichamen kan leiden tot vervreemding van het lichaam, maar kan ook stimuleren dat patiënten zich met beelden identificeren. De constructie van een bepaalde ervaring hangt af van de (in)compatibiliteit van de vertalingen van artsen en van patiënten. Ik stel voor om het idee van 'mediatie' te vervangen door Bruno Latour's concept van 'een lichaam dat leert geraakt te worden', omdat dat de lading van onderling verbonden interventies van real-time beeldvorming in belichaamde ervaring, beter dekt. Real-time beelden zijn geen afspiegeling van een lichamelijke toestand, noch vervreemden zij zonder meer lichaam van 'zelf': door real-time beeldvorming leren lichamen geraakt te worden.

De diffuse en tegenstrijdige ervaringen van patiënten die real-time medische beeldvorming ondergaan, vereisen een begrip van ziekte dat zowel de hermeneutische als ook de materiële en existentiële lagen van lichamelijkheid erkent en recht doet. In de laatste fase van de vertaling van beelden, zoals die in hoofdstuk 5 beschreven wordt, kan ziekte-ervaring net zomin onderscheiden worden van de medisch-professionele objectivering van een lichamelijke toestand als in de eerdere fases van voorbereiding en beeldproductie die in de voorgaande hoofdstukken werden beschreven. Als ze los van elkaar worden beschreven, kan de productie van medische kennis eenvoudig onderscheiden worden van de totstandkoming van ziekte-ervaring: het ene traject betreft de vertaling van beelden in geschreven taal, door middels van het lezen van beelden als datasets; in het andere traject worden beelden gelezen als plaatjes en vertaald in narratieve uitingen van ervaring. Door de trajecten niet parallel te beschrijven, maar in elkaars verlengde, is het echter mogelijk de coproductie van medische kennis en belichaamde ervaring te beschrijven, die resulteert in ziekte als een technologisch bemiddelde, gelaagde ervaring. Een analyse van technovisuele bemiddeling van belichaamde ervaring vraagt om een uitgebreide (ANT) beschrijving van de netwerken waarin lichamen ontstaan en ziekte circuleert als de referent van medische beelden, maar ook om een gedetailleerde (fenomenologische) weergave van hoe mensen die lichamen ervaren.

Mijn analyse van real-time medische beeldvorming ontkracht twee dominante stijlfiguren uit het publieke domein en het sociaal-wetenschappelijke vertoog: het beeld van het *transparante lichaam*, toegankelijk gemaakt en gecontroleerd door medische technologie; en het idee van medische technologieën die patiënten objectiveren en van hun lichaam *vervreemden*. Veel artsen zeggen dat patiënten onrealistische verwachtingen hebben van medische beeldvorming. Ik betoog dat medische praktijken zelf zulke hoge verwachtingen wekken. Artsen dragen bij aan het culturele vertoog van een 'transparant lichaam' door real-time beeldvorming voor te stellen in termen van 'kijken wat er mis is'. De ogenschijnlijk vanzelfsprekende mogelijkheid dat patiënten mee kunnen kijken op de monitor, is onderdeel van die praktijk. Als niet aan de verwachtingen van patiënten wordt voldaan, kan vervreemding inderdaad het gevolg zijn. Om dat te voorkomen, moeten artsen begrijpen dat het zien van beelden van hun eigen binnenkant voor veel patiënten een ingewikkelde ervaring is.

Mijn analyse kan misverstanden voorkomen door ervoor te zorgen dat die ingewikkelde ervaring begrijpelijk wordt. In een traject van verplaatsing en vertaling verkrijgen het lichaam en het fenomeen 'ziekte' verschillende hermeneutische, materiële en existentiële lagen. Ziekte is niet het resultaat van betekenisgeving, noch een inherente eigenschap van een lichaam: ziekte is een praktische zaak. Door medische antropologie te gebruiken om uitingen van ervaringen te beschrijven, actor-netwerk theorie om voorwaarden voor ervaring te traceren en postfenomenologie om de technologische bemiddeling van ervaring te begrijpen, heb ik een vocabulaire ontwikkeld om die gelaagde ervaring te kunnen analyseren als een vorm van *gedistribueerde lichamelijkheid*.

Voor patiënten is wat ze zien, horen en voelen tijdens een beeldvormend onderzoek vaak verwarrend en inconsistent. Een begrip als 'gedistribueerde lichamelijkheid' biedt een conceptuele strategie om met die inconsistentie om te gaan. Die strategie zou in de praktijk vertaald kunnen worden door in ziekenhuisbrochures informatie op te nemen om patiënten voor te bereiden op wat er op de monitor te zien is tijdens een onderzoek. Dat impliceert echter dat de kennis van patiënten beter aangepast moet worden aan biomedische kennis, om te komen tot een vorm van 'informed agency'. Dat is niet wat ik wil suggereren. Het vergroten van de macht en autonomie van patiënten door informatieverstrekking past in een discours van kiezen, dat tegenwoordig niet alleen in de gezondheidszorg dominant is. Een constructivistische benadering zoals ik die voorsta, past echter beter bij een discours van zorgen. Patiënten hebben er baat bij serieus genomen te worden als patiënten: als mensen die het vermogen tot handelen delen, eerder dan als mensen die autonomie hebben. Wat brochures en artsen zouden moeten doen, is expliciteren dat real-time medische beeldvorming een gezamenlijke inspanning is met beperkte mogelijkheden, die niet de werkelijkheid verbeeldt of objectieve kennis oplevert, maar wel aanwijzingen die in combinatie met andere aanwijzingen een diagnose kunnen opleveren. Dat vereist reflexieve medische praktijken, waaraan ik met dit boek hoop bij te dragen.

Curriculum Vitae

Maud Radstake (1973) studied cultural anthropology at the Catholic University (now Radboud University) Nijmegen and at the University of Amsterdam, where she specialized in medical anthropology. She wrote her Master's thesis on home-based for people living with HIV/AIDS in Ghana. In 1999 she obtained her MA degree (with honours). After having worked as a documentalist at the Metamedica department of the Free University in Amsterdam and as a project coordinator for the Nederlands Gesprek Centrum, she started a PhD at the Faculty of Arts and Culture of Maastricht University in 2001. She was a member of the department of Technology and Society Studies and of the research program Science, Society and Technology. Her PhD project was part of the NWO-funded research program The Mediated Body. She represented the PhD students in the board of the research school of Science, Technology and Modern Culture (WTMC) and in the faculty's research consultation council. She is member of the editorial board of the Graduate Journal of Social Science (GJSS). In April 2006 she accepted her current position as staff member Research & Dialogue at the Centre for Society and Genomics in Nijmegen.